AN INTRODUCTION TO
THE CHEMISTRY OF CARBOHYDRATES

AN INTRODUCTION TO
THE CHEMISTRY OF CARBOHYDRATES

R. D. GUTHRIE
READER IN CHEMISTRY
UNIVERSITY OF SUSSEX

AND

JOHN HONEYMAN
ASSISTANT DIRECTOR
SHIRLEY INSTITUTE, MANCHESTER

THIRD EDITION

CLARENDON PRESS · OXFORD
1968

Oxford University Press, Ely House, London W.1

GLASGOW NEW YORK TORONTO MELBOURNE WELLINGTON
CAPE TOWN SALISBURY IBADAN NAIROBI LUSAKA ADDIS ABABA
BOMBAY CALCUTTA MADRAS KARACHI LAHORE DACCA
KUALA LUMPUR HONG KONG TOKYO

FIRST EDITION 1948
SECOND EDITION 1964
THIRD EDITION 1968

PRINTED IN GREAT BRITAIN BY
WILLIAM CLOWES AND SONS, LIMITED
LONDON AND BECCLES

PREFACE TO THIRD EDITION

O U R aims have remained the same as in previous editions. Most chapters have been slightly modified, and that on physical methods has been lengthened. We have also added compounds of current interest to the chapter on miscellaneous derivatives. We have endeavoured to keep the book the same length as the previous edition.

April 1968 R.D.G.

J.H.

PREFACE TO THE SECOND EDITION

W E have tried to make the new edition concise and up-to-date, concentrating on important principles of carbohydrate chemistry. The increased use of physical methods and the interest in the shapes of molecules have caused us to add new chapters on these topics. No detailed references are given to the original literature but important review articles are listed at the end of appropriate chapters.

R.D.G.

J.H.

PREFACE TO THE FIRST EDITION

T H E aim of the author in writing this book has been to provide, in a compact form, an up-to-date account of the chemistry of a selected number of carbohydrates. No previous knowledge of the field is assumed, but the reader requires to be familiar with the elements of aliphatic and aromatic chemistry. The mono-saccharides are considered in detail in order to provide an adequate basis for studying farther the more complex carbo-hydrates. In addition to the crystalline di-, tri-, and tetra-saccharides, a few of the simpler polysaccharides of colloidal dimensions are discussed. The account of these does not claim to be exhaustive, but it is hoped that the introduction given here will enable the student to read, with greater ease, some of the more complete specialized studies now available.

While the material included provides a suitable course for students reading for an Honours degree in Chemistry, it is hoped that the book will appeal to a wider public. Academic and industrial chemists in related branches of organic chemistry who wish to keep abreast of recent developments in theory and technique should find the book of value.

It has been considered inappropriate to include numerous references to the original literature, but, in the case of many of the more important discoveries, the name of the author and the date are included. In this way the reader is introduced to most of the chief workers in the carbohydrate field. The original paper is easily located, when desired, by referring to the author index of *British (Chemical) Abstracts* or *Chemical Abstracts* for the appropriate year.

The author has to thank many friends for their assistance in making it possible for him to write this book. For help in the early, most difficult, years of his career he is grateful to Dr. James Scott, formerly Science Master at Riverside School, Stirling, and to Sir James C. Irvine, Principal and Vice-Chancellor of the University of St. Andrews. Professor D. H. Hey of the University of London, King's College, read the manuscript and made many valuable suggestions. The author has had the indispensable aid and co-operation of his wife in the preparation of this work for the press.

Chiswick, **1947**

CONTENTS

1

GENERAL INTRODUCTION

CARBOHYDRATES are among the most abundant constituents of plants and animals. They serve as sources of energy (sugars), and as stores of energy (starch and glycogen); they also form the major constituent (chitin) of the shells of crabs and lobsters, and the supporting tissue of plants (cellulose). Plants build up carbohydrates from carbon dioxide and water by photosynthesis, whereas animals have to rely on plants for their supplies, although given glucose they can convert this into glycogen, a more complex compound.

The name carbohydrate arose from the belief that each substance of this type had a molecular formula that could be expressed as $C_x(H_2O)_y$. Although true of the majority there are certain substances (e.g. deoxyhexoses, $C_6H_{12}O_5$) that do not conform to this formula but are classed as carbohydrates because of their chemical properties. A simplified definition of carbohydrates is that they are polyhydroxyaldehydes or ketones, or substances which may be hydrolysed by dilute acid to these compounds. This classification does not include compounds such as hexitols (hexahydroxyhexanes) and cyclitols (hexahydroxycyclohexanes), which are nevertheless conveniently studied alongside the carbohydrates.

Carbohydrates may be divided into two broad groups: sugars and polysaccharides.

Sugars are sweet, crystalline, and soluble in water. Their molecular weight is known exactly, and is invariable for a given substance. Sugars are classified as monosaccharides, disaccharides, trisaccharides, tetrasaccharides, &c., examples of all of which occur naturally. Monosaccharides cannot be hydrolysed to simpler sugars. Each molecule of a disaccharide, on hydrolysis with dilute acid, gives two monosaccharide molecules, for example:

$$\underset{\text{maltose}}{C_{12}H_{22}O_{11}} + H_2O \longrightarrow \underset{\text{glucose}}{2C_6H_{12}O_6}$$

A dissaccharide molecule, therefore, may be regarded as built up from two monosaccharide molecules with the elimination of one molecule of water. Tri- and tetra-saccharides are defined similarly. Oligosaccharides are sugars containing from two to about ten monosaccharide units.

Polysaccharides have the properties typical of high polymers. The molecular weight of any one may vary considerably, and in a given sample the molecules present will not all be of the same size. Hydrolysis with dilute acid produces many monosaccharide molecules from each molecule of polysaccharide.

THE CONSTITUTION AND CONFIGURATION OF THE MONOSACCHARIDES

CONSTITUTION OF THE MONOSACCHARIDES

THE monosaccharides are classified into triose, tetrose, &c., according to the number of carbon atoms in the molecule. Thus arabinose ($C_5H_{10}O_5$) is a pentose, glucose ($C_6H_{12}O_6$) is a hexose, and rhamnose ($C_6H_{12}O_5$) is a deoxyhexose.

Glucose, sometimes called dextrose, is the commonest monosaccharide, occurring free in the juice of fruits and in honey. Many disaccharides and polysaccharides give glucose on hydrolysis, e.g. maltose, cellulose, and starch.

The constitution of glucose has been determined by the following method.

(i) Elementary analysis and molecular weight determination established the molecular formula as $C_6H_{12}O_6$ (Tollens 1888).

(ii) Acetylation led to a crystalline penta-acetate, showing that glucose has five hydroxyl groups (Franchimont 1879, 1892). The stability of glucose suggests that the grouping —CH(OH)$_2$ is absent and therefore that five of the carbon atoms bear one hydroxyl group each.

(iii) Reaction with hydrogen cyanide, followed by hydrolysis of the resulting cyanohydrin, produced an acid that was reduced by red phosphorus and hydriodic acid to heptanoic acid (Kiliani 1886). This shows the presence of an aldehyde group and, also, that the carbon chain is unbranched.

The structural formula on p. 4 is the only one that explains these reactions.

Glucose is a polyhydroxyaldehyde or aldose, or more particularly an aldohexose, i.e. a monosaccharide with one aldehyde group and a total of six carbon atoms in its molecule.

Fructose, sometimes called lævulose, is another common sugar and is frequently found with glucose in fruits. The

```
 CHO                  CN                      CO2H                    CO2H
  |                   |                        |                       |
 CHOH                CHOH                     CHOH                     CH2
  |        HCN        |        hydrolysis      |          P/HI         |
 CHOH     ──→        CHOH     ─────────→      CHOH        ──→          CH2
  |                   |                        |                       |
 CHOH                CHOH                     CHOH                     CH2
  |                   |                        |                       |
 CHOH                CHOH                     CHOH                     CH2
  |                   |                        |                       |
 CH2OH               CH2OH                    CH2OH                    CH3
 glucose                                                          heptanoic acid
```

polysaccharide, inulin, which occurs in certain tubers (e.g. dandelion, dahlia) can be hydrolysed to fructose.

The constitution of fructose has been determined by the method used for glucose.

Identical results were obtained from (i) and (ii) above, whereas (iii) led to 2-methylhexanoic acid. Thus fructose has an unbranched chain of six carbon atoms, five of which each carry a hydroxyl group, while the sixth is part of a carbonyl group situated next to a terminal carbon atom (Kiliani 1886).

```
 CH2OH               CH2OH                    CH2OH                    CH3
  |                   |                        |                       |
 CO                  C(OH)CN                  C(OH)CO2H                CH·CO2H
  |                   |                        |                       |
 CHOH                CHOH                     CHOH                     CH2
  |        HCN        |        hydrolysis      |          P/HI         |
 CHOH     ──→        CHOH     ─────────→      CHOH        ──→          CH2
  |                   |                        |                       |
 CHOH                CHOH                     CHOH                     CH2
  |                   |                        |                       |
 CH2OH               CH2OH                    CH2OH                    CH3
 fructose                                                    2-methylhexanoic acid
```

Fructose is a polyhydroxyketone, a ketose, and, more particularly, a ketohexose. In general, the naturally occurring ketoses have the ketone group attached to a terminal carbon atom.

The structure of all monosaccharides may be established similarly.

The numbering convention, which is shown for the hexoses but which applies throughout, should be noted. The carbon atom marked 1 is referred to as $C_{(1)}$; the others are denoted similarly. The aldehyde group of aldoses is always regarded as being in position 1, the keto group of the ketoses shown being in position 2.

The known deoxy-sugars include the 6-deoxyaldohexoses, for example rhamnose and fucose, which have the same structures

	Trioses	Tetroses	Pentoses	Hexoses
Aldose	CHO | *CHOH | CH$_2$OH	CHO | *CHOH | *CHOH | CH$_2$OH	CHO | *CHOH | *CHOH | *CHOH | CH$_2$OH	1. CHO 2. *CHOH 3. *CHOH 4. *CHOH 5. *CHOH 6. CH$_2$OH
Ketose	CH$_2$OH | CO | CH$_2$OH	CH$_2$OH | CO | *CHOH | CH$_2$OH	CH$_2$OH | CO | *CHOH | *CHOH | CH$_2$OH	1. CH$_2$OH 2. CO 3. *CHOH 4. *CHOH 5. *CHOH 6. CH$_2$OH

* Represents an asymmetric carbon atom.

as aldohexoses except that the terminal group is —CH$_3$ instead of —CH$_2$OH (see p. 85).

REACTIONS OF MONOSACCHARIDES

Many, but not all, of the reactions of the carbonyl group of aldoses and ketoses are similar to those of simple aliphatic aldehydes and ketones. For instance, both aldoses *and* ketoses reduce Fehling's solution and Tollens' reagent (ammoniacal silver nitrate), but neither affects Schiff's reagent.

Only a few reactions are considered here, but others are dealt with later in the book.

Reduction

Early workers used sodium amalgam, which is slow and sometimes causes interconversions. The modern industrial methods

CHO
|
(CHOH)$_4$ $\longrightarrow$
|
CH$_2$OH

glucose

CH$_2$OH
|
(CHOH)$_4$
|
CH$_2$OH

sorbitol

CH$_2$OH
|
CO
|
(CHOH)$_3$ $\longrightarrow$
|
CH$_2$OH

fructose

CH$_2$OH
|
*CHOH
|
(CHOH)$_3$
|
CH$_2$OH

sorbitol
mannitol

are electrolytic reduction or high-pressure hydrogenation using a nickel or copper chromite catalyst. Treatment of an aqueous solution of the sugar with sodium borohydride is the best laboratory method. Reduction of fructose leads to the formation of an additional asymmetric carbon atom (*). The two hexitols are obtained in unequal amounts.

Oxidation

Aldoses may be gently oxidized, for example by bromine water, to the corresponding *aldonic acid*, which readily gives a stable γ-lactone, usually obtained by evaporating aqueous solutions. The lactone may be reduced by sodium amalgam in the presence of a trace of acid to the original aldose (Fischer 1889).

CHO	CO_2H	CO	CH_2OH
CHOH	CHOH	α CHOH	CHOH
CHOH —[O]→	CHOH →	β CHOH	→ CHOH
CHOH	CHOH	γ CH——O	CHOH
CHOH	CHOH	δ CHOH	CHOH
CH_2OH	CH_2OH	CH_2OH	CH_2OH
aldose (e.g. glucose)	aldonic acid (gluconic acid)	aldonolactone (glucono-γ-lactone)	alditol (sorbitol)

Addition of an aqueous solution of sodium borohydride to the lactone in water yields the corresponding sugar, but addition of the aqueous lactone to aqueous borohydride gives the alditol (Wolfrom 1951).

Oxidation by hypoiodite is used for the quantitative determination of aldoses (Ingles and Israel 1948).

Ketoses are not oxidized by bromine water. Stronger oxidants usually break the carbon chain (cf. ketones), although sorbose (a ketohexose) has been oxidized with nitric acid to give a rather low yield of the corresponding keto-acid (Haworth 1934).

CH_2OH	CO_2H
CO	CO
$(CHOH)_3$ →	$(CHOH)_3$
CH_2OH	CH_2OH
sorbose	

More drastic oxidation of aldoses, for example by nitric acid, gives a dicarboxylic acid, called a saccharic, or more systematically, an aldaric acid, which can be isolated as the di-lactone.

CHO CO_2H CO
| | |
CHOH   CHOH   α   CHOH
| | |
CHOH HNO_3 CHOH   γβ   CH
| | |
CHOH   CHOH   βγ   CH
| | |
CHOH   CHOH   α   CHOH
| | |
CH_2OH CO_2H CO

aldose   aldaric acid
(e.g.glucose)   (glucaric or saccharic acid)

Reaction with phenylhydrazine

Ketoses and aldoses react normally with phenylhydrazine (one molecular proportion) to give phenylhydrazones, but with excess of phenylhydrazine (three molecular proportions) osazones are formed together with aniline and ammonia (Fischer 1884). This reaction is discussed on p. 78.

Since glucose and fructose give the same osazone it follows that they have the same configuration on $C_{(3)}$, $C_{(4)}$, and $C_{(5)}$. Mannose, another aldohexose, also gives glucosazone, showing that glucose and mannose are identical except for the configuration at $C_{(2)}$. Compounds that differ only in the configuration

CHO   CH:N·NHPh
| | NH_3
CHOH   CHOH   +
| | $PhNH_2$
$(CHOH)_3$ $(CHOH)_3$ +
| | CH:N·NHPh
CH_2OH CH_2OH |
glucose   glucose   C:N·NHPh
     phenylhydrazone |
CH_2OH CH_2OH $(CHOH)_3$
| | |
CO   C:N·NHPh CH_2OH
| | glucosazone
$(CHOH)_3$ $(CHOH)_3$
| |
CH_2OH CH_2OH
fructose   fructose
     phenylhydrazone

at one carbon atom are called *epimers*; glucose and mannose are $C_{(2)}$-epimers.

Reaction with hydrogen cyanide

The carbonyl groups of ketoses and aldoses react normally with hydrogen cyanide to give cyanohydrins (see p. 3).

CONFIGURATION OF THE MONOSACCHARIDES

From 1891 to 1896 Fischer, basing his investigation on the new ideas of stereochemistry put forward independently by Le Bel and van't Hoff, attacked the problem of aldose configuration. It was known that isomers could exist of molecules containing an asymmetric carbon atom (i.e. an atom to which four different atoms or groups are attached). These stereoisomers are known as optical isomers and differ only in the arrangement of the groups in space. In glyceraldehyde the groups attached to the asymmetric carbon atom (*) can be considered to be at the vertices of a regular tetrahedron. The diagram shows the two non-superimposable stereoisomeric molecules, which are

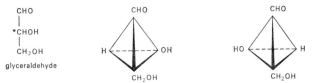

mirror images. Solutions of compounds like this, which have asymmetric molecules, rotate the plane of plane-polarized light; these compounds are said to be 'optically active'.

For aldoses and ketoses the number of optically active isomers is 2^n, where n is the number of dissimilar asymmetric carbon atoms. There are 2^{n-1} enantiomorphic (mirror-image) pairs. The table shows the number of optical isomers and enantiomorphic pairs for the monosaccharides up to the hexoses.

Sugar	Number of asymmetric carbon atoms	Number of optical isomers	Number of enantiomorphic pairs
Aldotrioses	1	2	1
Aldotetroses and ketopentoses	2	4	2
Aldopentoses and ketohexoses	3	8	4
Aldohexoses	4	16	8

Fischer derived planar formulae for the tetroses and higher aldoses, by considering that the lower edges of the tetrahedra forming the carbon chain all lay in a straight line in the plane of the paper as shown below. (The dotted line represents this invisible lower edge.) The projection of this three-dimensional formula on to the plane of the paper gives the planar Fischer projection formula. This is illustrated by the tetrose (1) and pentose (2) shown below.

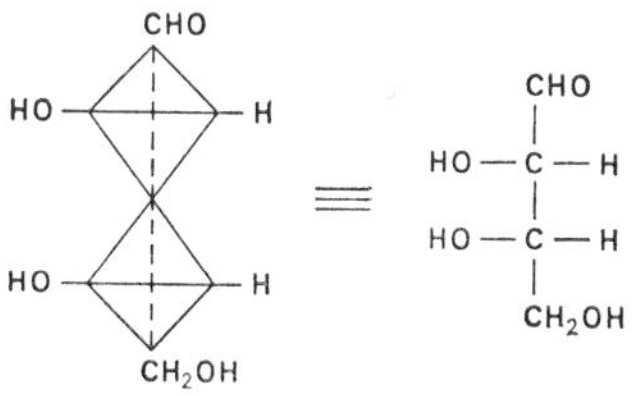

(1) 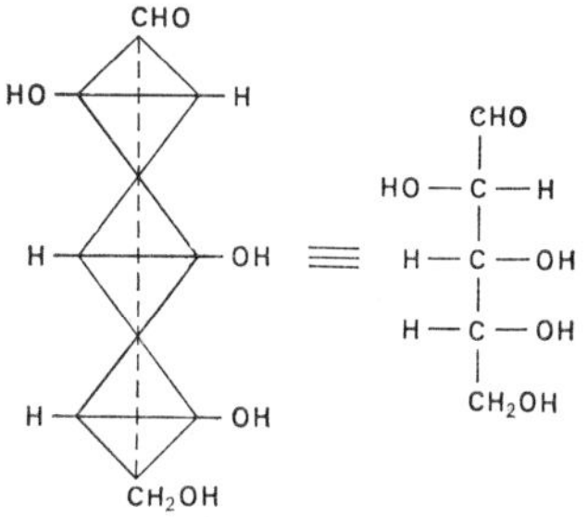   (2)

Attention is drawn to the limitation of Fischer projection formulae. In modern terms, such projections are those of molecules in their least stable, fully eclipsed conformation. The apparent *cis* or *trans* relationship of neighbouring groups does not necessarily occur in the *actual* shape of the molecule.

Fischer differentiated between enantiomorphic pairs of aldoses by using the symbols *d* and *l* for dextrorotatory and laevorotatory. This system of nomenclature was soon replaced by that of Rosanoff (1906) who proposed that sugars having the hydroxyl group on the bottom asymmetric carbon atom to the right of the carbon chain should be called δ-sugars, and those with it to the left, λ-sugars. These symbols were later changed to D and L respectively, and these are now universally used. Thus for the simplest sugar, glyceraldehyde, the two enantiomers have the structures shown below. Also, (1) above is an L-tetrose and (2) is a D-pentose. Naturally occurring

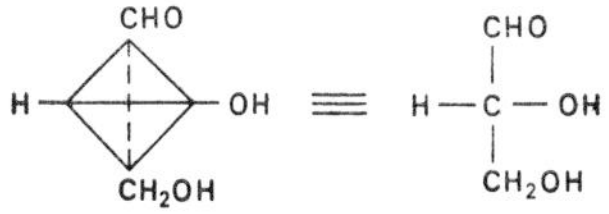

D-glyceraldehyde 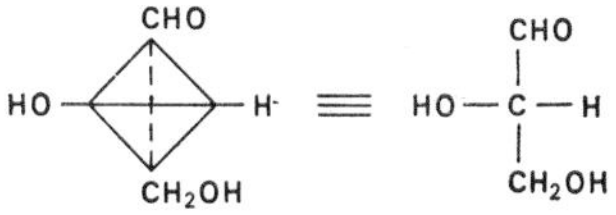   L-glyceraldehyde

glucose has the reference hydroxyl group to the right on the Fischer projection formula and so the compound is called D-glucose. It must be stressed that D- and L- are quite independent of the sign of rotation, which is shown by $(+)$ or $(-)$ where necessary. For example, the naturally occurring dextrorotatory pentose, arabinose, is described as L$(+)$-arabinose. A mixture of equal amounts of D- and L-form of the same compound is called a racemic mixture or a DL-mixture.

It is stressed that the structure assigned to, for example, D$(+)$-glyceraldehyde was only by convention since Rosanoff did not know its *absolute* configuration. X-ray studies (Bijvoet 1954) showed that the absolute configuration of L$(+)$-tartaric acid was identical with the structure that had been arbitrarily assigned to it. Because it has now been shown that D-glyceraldehyde and the D-sugars generally have the same relative configuration as D$(-)$-tartaric acid it follows that the D-sugars also have the absolute configuration previously written arbitrarily for them.

Fischer's ingenious solution of the problem of assigning configurations to the aldoses is now illustrated by consideration of the structure of D-glucose. In the ensuing proof modern symbols and names are used.

Natural glucose was arbitrarily assigned to the D-series and hence it has partial structure (3). (Later work showed that it could be synthesized from D-glyceraldehyde and hence this assumption was fortunately correct.) D-Glucose and naturally occurring mannose give the same phenylosazone and are therefore $C_{(2)}$-epimers. This enables structures (4) and (5) to be proposed for these two sugars, though it is not known which is which. The configurations at $C_{(3)}$ and $C_{(4)}$ have also to be determined.

```
      CHO                CHO            CH:N·NHPh             CHO
       |                  |                |                  |
    (CHOH)₃             HCOH            C:N·NHPh            HOCH
       |                  |                |                  |
     HCOH              (CHOH)₂  ──→     (CHOH)₂   ←──      (CHOH)₂
       |                  |                |                  |
     CH₂OH              CHOH             HCOH               HCOH
                          |                |                  |
       (3)              CH₂OH            CH₂OH              CH₂OH
                         (4)              (5)                (5)
```

Treatment of naturally occurring arabinose with hydrogen cyanide, followed by hydrolysis, gave the monobasic acids

L-gluconic and L-mannonic acids, the mirror images of the ones obtained by oxidation of D-mannose and D-glucose. The two corresponding D-acids would therefore be obtained from D-arabinose. Also L-arabinose, on oxidation with nitric acid, gave an *optically active* dibasic acid, L-arabinaric acid, showing that the hydroxyl group on $C_{(2)}$ must be on the opposite side of the carbon chain to that on $C_{(5)}$; L-arabinaric acid is therefore (6),

<pre>
   CO₂H   CHO   CHO   CHO
    | | | |
  HCOH   HOCH   HOCH   HCOH
    | | | |
  CHOH   CHOH   HOCH   HOCH
    | | | |
  HOCH   HCOH   CHOH   CHOH
    | | | |
   CO₂H   CH₂OH   HCOH   HCOH
                              CH₂OH   CH₂OH
   (6)   (7)   (8)   (9)
</pre>

and D-arabinose is (7). Since this pentose gives derivatives of both D-glucose and D-mannose, these must be (8) or (9).

The two dibasic acids obtained by oxidizing D-mannose and D-glucose with nitric acid are (10) and (11). Since both acids are optically active neither (10) nor (11) can be symmetrical, and so the $C_{(4)}$-hydroxyl group is to the right. Therefore D-glucose and D-mannose are (12) or (13) but it is still necessary to decide which is which.

<pre>
   CO₂H   CO₂H   CHO   CHO
    | | | |
  HOCH   HCOH   HOCH   HCOH
    | | | |
  HOCH   HOCH   HOCH   HOCH
    | | | |
  CHOH   CHOH   HCOH   HCOH
    | | | |
  HCOH   HCOH   HCOH   HCOH
    | | | |
   CO₂H   CO₂H   CH₂OH   CH₂OH
   (10)   (11)   (12)   (13)
</pre>

D-Glucaric acid was also obtained from another aldohexose, gulose, by oxidation with nitric acid. This means that gulose is

<pre>
  CH₂OH   CHO   CH₂OH   CHO
    | | | |
  HOCH   HOCH   HCOH   HOCH
    | | | |
  HOCH   HOCH   HOCH   HOCH
    | ≡ | | ≡ |
  HCOH   HCOH   HCOH   HCOH
    | | | |
  HCOH   HCOH   HCOH   HOCH
    | | | |
   CHO   CH₂OH   CHO   CH₂OH
   (14)   (15)
</pre>

the same as D-glucose except that the —CHO and —CH$_2$OH groups are interchanged. The two aldoses obtained by doing this to (12) and (13) are, respectively, (14) and (15). But (12) and (14) are identical and the dibasic acid (16) can only be formed by the oxidation of *one* aldohexose, namely (12). The dibasic acid

```
     CO₂H              CO₂H
      |                 |
     HOCH              HCOH
      |                 |
     HOCH              HOCH
      |                 |
     HCOH              HCOH
      |                 |
     HCOH              HCOH
      |                 |
     CO₂H              CO₂H
     (16)              (17)
```

(17) can be formed from the two aldohexoses, (13) and (15), and is therefore D-glucaric acid. Consequently D-glucose is (13), D-mannose is (12), and L-gulose is (15).

Similar reasoning enabled the structures of all the aldoses to be deduced.

Each ketose has one asymmetric carbon atom fewer than the corresponding aldose. This means that there are eight keto-hexoses (four enantiomorphic pairs). Their configurations may be deduced from the fact that they give phenylosazones identical with those obtained from the corresponding aldohexoses.

```
     CH₂OH
      |
      CO
      |
     HOCH
      |
     HCOH
      |
     HCOH
      |
     CH₂OH
   D-fructose
```

The structures of all the aldoses from the D-trioses to the D-hexoses and of the D-ketopentoses and -hexoses are set out in the sheet inside the back cover.

A simpler way of drawing sugar structures is to use the diagrammatic formula shown on p. 13, using horizontal lines to show the positions of the hydroxyl groups on the asymmetric carbon atoms and omitting the hydrogen atoms.

The structures of the aldopentoses and aldohexoses can be

remembered by the use of mnemonics. The initial letters of the former make the 'word' RAXL. Drawing four backbone formulae (i.e. (18)), one writes the names of the sugars in the mnemonic order and then inserts in each the $C_{(4)}$-hydroxyl group

```
      CHO              CHO
       |                |
      HCOH             ──
       |                |
      HOCH             ──│
       |                |
      HCOH             ──
       |                |
      HCOH             ──
       |                |
     CH₂OH            CH₂OH
```

on the right for the D-series. The $C_{(3)}$-hydroxyl group is placed two to the right and then two to the left. The $C_{(2)}$-hydroxyl group is placed alternately right and left. Thus

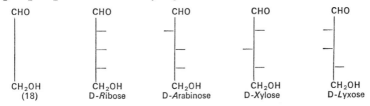

```
 CHO        CHO        CHO        CHO        CHO
  |          |          |          |          |

CH₂OH      CH₂OH      CH₂OH      CH₂OH      CH₂OH
 (18)     D-Ribose   D-Arabinose  D-Xylose  D-Lyxose
```

The D-aldohexoses may be built up in a similar way using a mnemonic conceived by the Drs. Fieser: '*All altruists gladly make gum in gallon tanks.*' Again the $C_{(5)}$-hydroxyl group is to

```
 CHO        CHO        CHO        CHO

CH₂OH      CH₂OH      CH₂OH      CH₂OH
Allose     Altrose    Glucose    Mannose

 CHO        CHO        CHO        CHO

CH₂OH      CH₂OH      CH₂OH      CH₂OH
Gulose     Idose      Galactose  Talose
```

the right; of the $C_{(4)}$-hydroxyl groups the first four are to the right, the next four to the left; the $C_{(3)}$-hydroxyl groups are in pairs to the right and to the left; the $C_{(2)}$-hydroxyl groups are alternately right and left.

REVIEW

The halogen oxidation of simple carbohydrates, by J. W. Green, *Adv. Carbohyd. Chem.* 1948, **3**, 129.

3

SYNTHESIS OF MONOSACCHARIDES

BEFORE considering the complete synthesis of monosaccharides, processes for the interconversion of sugars will be described. These have been of considerable use in synthesizing and proving the structures of aldoses and ketoses.

Conversion of an aldose into the corresponding ketose

Phenylhydrazine residues may be removed from phenylosazones with fairly concentrated acids or with benzaldehyde in dilute acid to yield 2-ketoaldoses or osones. The aldehyde group is more readily reduced than the keto group, so that treatment of the osone with zinc and acetic acid produces the ketose in fair yield (Fischer).

```
CHO            CH:N·NHPh        CHO            CH₂OH
 |              |                 |              |
|—             C:N·NHPh         |—=O          |—=O
 |              |                 |              |
|—      →      |—      →        |—      →      |—
 |              |                 |              |
|—             |—               |—             |—
 |              |                 |              |
CH₂OH          CH₂OH            CH₂OH          CH₂OH
D-glucose      D-glucosazone    D-glucosone    D-fructose
```

Another method, not used extensively, consists of heating the aldose in aqueous pyridine. This yields an equilibrium mixture of the original aldose and a small amount of the corresponding ketose. Some of the aldose may be separated by crystallization, and the rest oxidized by bromine water to the aldonic acid, which is then precipitated as the barium salt. In this way the rare ketose, allulose, has been prepared from allose (H. O. L. Fischer 1927). Anhydrous pyridine has been shown to have no effect (Courtois 1960).

Conversion of an aldose into the next higher ketose

In this method the aldose is oxidized to the corresponding aldonic acid, which is acetylated and then converted into the acid chloride with thionyl chloride. Treatment of this with dia-zomethane followed by heating with aqueous acetic acid and,

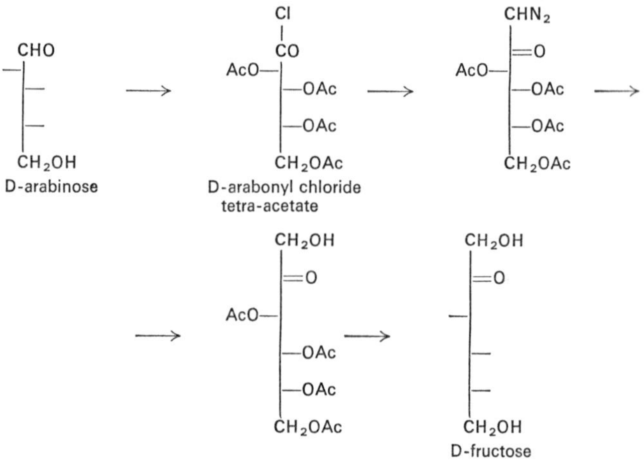

finally, deacetylation by alkaline hydrolysis gives the higher ketose (Wolfrom 1941).

Ascent of the aldose series

Treatment of, for example, a pentose with hydrogen cyanide, followed by hydrolysis, gives a mixture of two $C_{(2)}$-epimeric hexonic acids in unequal quantities. These acids are separated as their crystalline lactones, which are readily reduced to the corresponding hexoses (see p. 6). The epimeric hexonic acids are produced in unequal amounts because a new asymmetric centre has been introduced into an already asymmetric mole-cule.

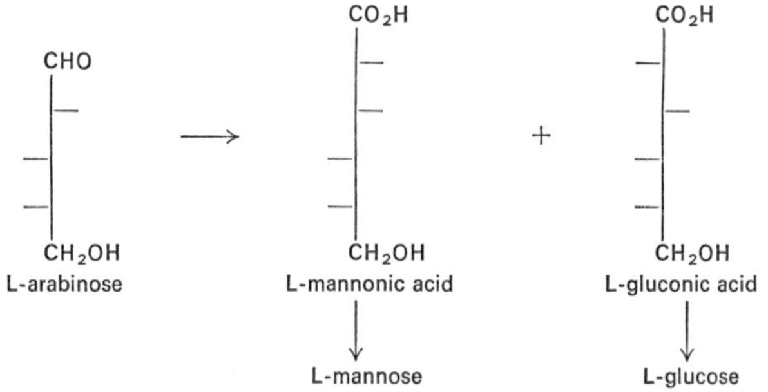

There is no limit, in theory, to the size of the monosaccharide molecule that can be built up in this way. In practice, however, there are two products to separate and purify at each stage; often it is very difficult to induce the compounds to crystallize. From D-glucose, a crystalline D-decose has been prepared (Philippe 1911), while a crystalline D-nonose has been obtained from D-mannose (Fischer).

Nitromethane reacts with aliphatic aldehydes in the presence of sodium methoxide to yield two epimeric *aci*nitro salts containing one more carbon atom than the aldehyde (Henry 1895). These salts are converted into the *C*-nitroalcohols by dilute acid and into the corresponding aldehyde by more concentrated acid.

$$R \cdot CHO + MeNO_2 \xrightarrow{\text{MeONa}} \underset{\text{2 epimers}}{R \cdot CHOH \cdot CH:NO_2^- Na^+} \xrightarrow{H^+}$$

$$R \cdot CHOH \cdot CH_2NO_2$$

$$\downarrow H^+$$

$$R \cdot CHOH \cdot CHO$$

Treatment of a sugar with nitromethane gives two epimeric *C*-nitroalcohols, which are separated by fractional crystallization and then each converted into the aldose (Sowden and H. O. L. Fischer 1947). Again the epimers are formed in unequal amounts.

An amorphous nonose has been synthesized by this method (Sowden 1960).

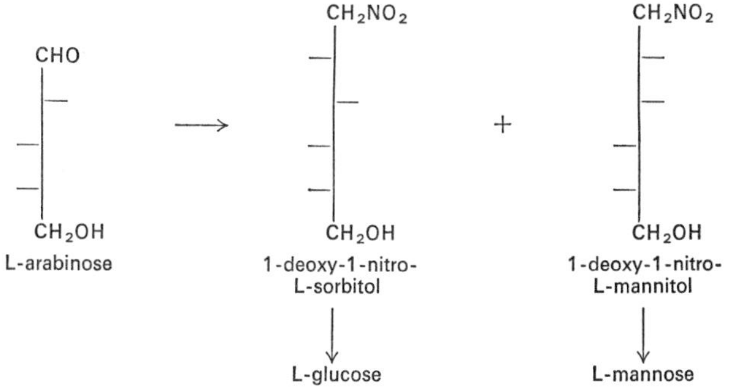

CHO	CH₂NO₂	CH₂NO₂
L-arabinose	1-deoxy-1-nitro-L-sorbitol	1-deoxy-1-nitro-L-mannitol
	L-glucose	L-mannose

Conversion of a ketose into the corresponding aldose

The reduction of D-fructose to D-sorbitol and D-mannitol has already been described (see p. 5). The alcohols may be separated and by careful oxidation converted partly into

D-gluconic and D-mannonic acids, respectively, although since oxidation can take place at $C_{(6)}$ as well as at $C_{(1)}$ a mixture of products is obtained. The acids are converted into the aldoses by lactonization followed by reduction.

Epimerization

If an aldonic acid is heated to $140°–150°$ in aqueous pyridine or quinoline, epimerization occurs on $C_{(2)}$ to give an equilibrium mixture of the two $C_{(2)}$-epimeric hexonic acids. The acids may then be separated, converted into the lactones, and reduced to the original aldose and its $C_{(2)}$-epimer.

CHO	CO$_2$H	CO$_2$H	CHO
D-glucose	D-gluconic acid	D-mannonic acid	D-mannose

Descent of the aldose series

The processes for doing this often involve removal of $C_{(1)}$, and the conversion of $C_{(2)}$ to an aldehyde group. Hence a pair of aldoses epimeric on $C_{(2)}$ give, when degraded, the same lower aldose.

The oldest method (Wohl 1893) involves heating the aldose oxime with acetic anhydride in the presence of zinc chloride or sodium acetate, so that the oxime group is dehydrated and the hydroxyl groups are esterified (see p. 53) to give the acetylated acid nitrile. With ammoniacal silver oxide the nitrile group is removed and acetamide, produced from the acetate groups, reacts with the new aldose to give its diacetamido derivative; the free aldose is then obtained by hydrolysis. The yield is higher when sodium methoxide in chloroform is used instead of ammoniacal silver oxide. The mechanism of this reaction has been studied (Isbell 1949).

Another method is to add hydrogen peroxide and a trace of a ferrous salt as catalyst (Fenton's reagent) to the calcium salt of an aldonic acid (Ruff 1898). In this way calcium D-gluconate

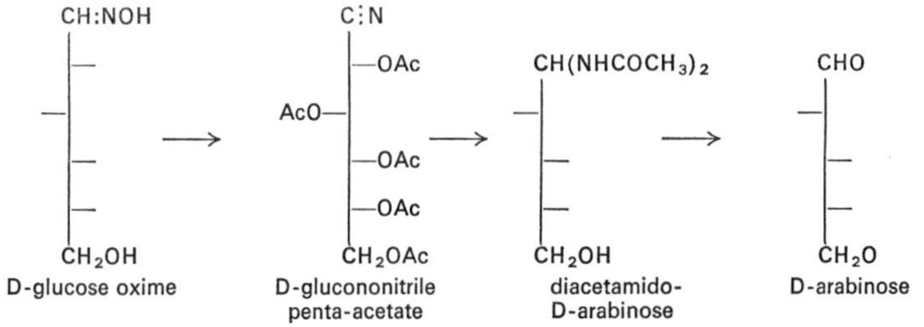

CH:NOH $\longrightarrow$ C:N, AcO—, —OAc, —OAc, —OAc, CH$_2$OAc $\longrightarrow$ CH(NHCOCH$_3$)$_2$, CH$_2$OH $\longrightarrow$ CHO, CH$_2$O

D-glucose oxime   D-gluconitrile penta-acetate   diacetamido-D-arabinose   D-arabinose

is converted into D-arabinose. The yield is rather low because further degradation occurs.

The Hofmann reaction for converting an amide into an amine has been adapted for this purpose (Weerman 1915). An alkaline solution containing hypochlorite converts the amide of an aldonic acid into the lower aldose and sodium isocyanate. This reaction is not always practicable, due to the difficulty of preparing the acid amide by the action of ammonia on the aldonolactone.

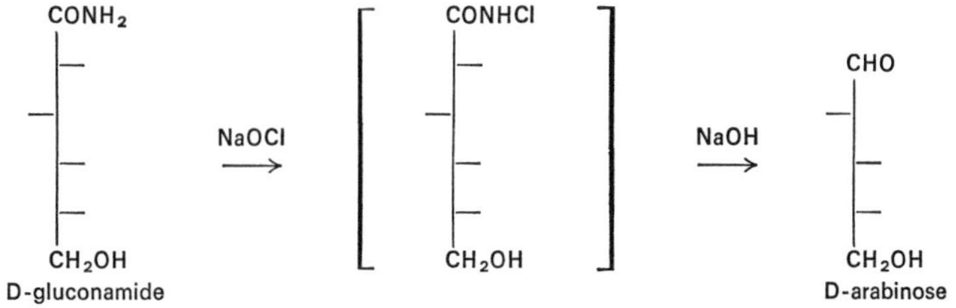

CONH$_2$ — — — CH$_2$OH   D-gluconamide

$\xrightarrow{\text{NaOCl}}$

[CONHCl — — — CH$_2$OH]

$\xrightarrow{\text{NaOH}}$

CHO — — CH$_2$OH   D-arabinose

Similar degradation occurs during the storage of D-glucose labelled at C$_{(1)}$ with ^{14}C (Bourne 1960).

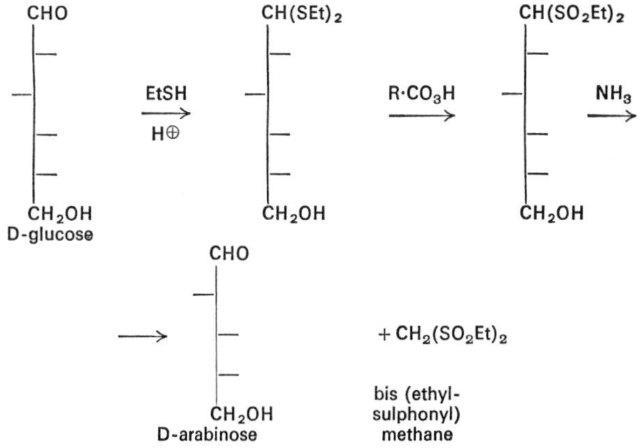

CHO — — — CH$_2$OH   D-glucose

$\xrightarrow[\text{H}\oplus]{\text{EtSH}}$

CH(SEt)$_2$ — — — CH$_2$OH

$\xrightarrow{\text{R·CO}_3\text{H}}$

CH(SO$_2$Et)$_2$ — — — CH$_2$OH

$\xrightarrow{\text{NH}_3}$

$\longrightarrow$

CHO — — CH$_2$OH   D-arabinose

+ CH$_2$(SO$_2$Et)$_2$

bis (ethyl-sulphonyl) methane

A more recent degradative method (see formulae on p. 19) is based on the oxidation of a sugar mercaptal (see p. 50) with a peracid to the bis(ethylsulphonyl) derivative, which gives the lower aldose on treatment with aqueous ammonia (MacDonald and H. O. L. Fischer 1947, Hough 1954).

Fermentation

The only aldoses and ketoses that are fermented by yeasts are D-glucose, D-mannose, D-fructose, and, less readily, D-galactose. This illustrates how closely yeast activity is dependent upon configuration.

Complete synthesis of the monosaccharides

The action of dilute alkali on formaldehyde produces a sweet syrup which was called 'formose' (Butleroff 1861, Leow 1886). This syrup was found to be a mixture of ketoses and aldoses from which DL-glucosazone was isolated.

The action of dilute alkali on acrolein dibromide does not give the expected glyceraldehyde, but leads to a sweet syrup named 'acrose'. DL-Glyceraldehyde is produced initially; this is partially converted in the presence of alkali (see p. 41) into the isomeric dihydroxyacetone. The alkali then further induces an aldol condensation to yield a mixture of ketohexoses.

$$
\begin{array}{ccccccc}
 & & & & CH_2OH & & CH_2OH \\
 & & & & | & & | \\
 & & & & CO & & CO \\
 & & & & | & & | \\
CHO & & CHO & & CH_2OH & & CHOH \\
| & & | & & + & & | \\
CHBr & \longrightarrow & CHOH & \longrightarrow & CHO & \longrightarrow & CHOH \\
| & & | & & | & & | \\
CH_2Br & & CH_2OH & & CHOH & & CHOH \\
 & & & & | & & | \\
 & & & & CH_2OH & & CH_2OH \\
\text{acrolein} & & & & & & \text{'acrose'} \\
\text{dibromide} & & & & & &
\end{array}
$$

Two distinct phenylosazones, α-acrosazone and β-acrosazone, were isolated from the syrupy product (Fischer 1887). The former was shown to be DL-glucosazone, proving that α-acrose was DL-fructose. Later, β-acrose was proved to be DL-sorbose (Schmitz 1913).

The conversion of α-acrose (DL-fructose) into naturally occurring monosaccharides is somewhat involved, but was successfully carried out using the reactions already described (Fischer).

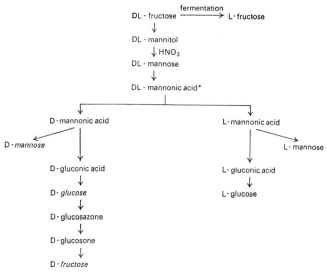

DL - fructose $\xrightarrow{\text{fermentation}}$ L - fructose
↓
DL - mannitol
↓ HNO₃
DL - mannose
↓
DL - mannonic acid*

D - mannonic acid ⟶ L - mannonic acid

D - *mannose* ⟵ D - mannonic acid   L - mannonic acid ⟶ L - mannose

D - gluconic acid   L - gluconic acid
↓   ↓
D - *glucose*   L - glucose
↓
D - glucosazone
↓
D - glucosone
↓
D - *fructose*

The naturally occurring sugars are italicized
*Separated by fractional crystallization of the strychnine salts

It is interesting to note that when Emil Fischer started work in carbohydrate chemistry (1886) the only monosaccharides known were L-arabinose, D-glucose, D-galactose, D-fructose, and L-sorbose, all occurring naturally. L-Arabinose was obtained from cherry gum by acid hydrolysis (Kiliani). D-Galactose,

Physical properties of some naturally occurring monosaccharides

	Main source	m.p.	[α]$_D$ in water	
D-ribose	nucleic acids	87°	−23° →	−24°
D-xylose	xylan	145	+94 →	+19
L-arabinose	gums	160	+190 →	+105
D-glucose	starch	146	+112 →	+53
D-mannose	mannan	133	+29 →	+14
D-galactose	gums	167	+150 →	+80
L-rhamnose	glycosides	124	−9 →	−8
L-fucose	seaweeds	145	−153 →	−76
D-fructose	inulin	102	−132 →	−94
L-sorbose	rowans	159	−44 →	−43
D-tagatose	gums	134	−3 →	−5

together with D-glucose, was obtained by hydrolysing lactose, the sugar of mammalian milk, whilst L-sorbose had been obtained from the fermented and bacterially oxidized juice of rowan berries, *Sorbus aucuparia L.* (Pelouse 1852). The sources of D-glucose and D-fructose have already been mentioned. Before Fischer's death in 1919, fourteen of the possible sixteen aldohexoses had been prepared and characterized; Fischer and his co-workers were responsible for twelve. The remaining two were isolated later (Austin 1934). The reactions employed in the preparation of all the aldoses have been the simple ones of degradation, oxidation, epimerization, and cyanohydrin formation followed by hydrolysis, lactonization, and reduction.

REVIEW

The Fischer cyanohydrin synthesis, by C. S. Hudson, *Adv. Carbohyd. Chem.* 1945, **1**, 1.

4

THE RING STRUCTURE OF
MONOSACCHARIDES

Evidence for the presence of a ring
in monosaccharides

IN this section the case of D-glucose is discussed in detail, but the same argument applies to all the pentoses and hexoses. On the basis of the reactions already described an open-chain or acyclic structure has been postulated, but evidence will now be presented to show that this is inadequate.

1. The fact that a solution of D-glucose does not colour Schiff's reagent suggests that the aldehyde group is masked in some way.

2. The specific rotation, $[\alpha]$, of a freshly prepared aqueous solution of D-glucose changes rapidly until it reaches a constant value. This phenomenon is known as *mutarotation*. Anhydrous D-glucose exists in two forms, differing in melting-point, initial $[\alpha]$, and solubility. The more common form, α-D-glucose, has an initial $[\alpha]_D$ in water of $+113°$, falling to a constant value of $+52·5°$. The other form, which separates from a saturated aqueous solution at temperatures above 115°, is β-D-glucose, which has an $[\alpha]_D$ of $+19°$ rising to the same constant value of $+52·5°$. Thus solution of either in water leads to the same equilibrium mixture containing the two forms. The existence of these two distinct isomers cannot be explained by an open-chain formula.

3. D-Glucose penta-acetate and pentabenzoate do not react with hydroxylamine, showing the absence of a free aldehyde group.

4. A normal aldehyde reacts with methanolic hydrogen chloride to give a dimethyl acetal:

$$R·CHO \xrightarrow[(-H_2O)]{MeOH/HCl} R·CH(OMe)_2$$

D-Glucose, however, when boiled with methanol containing hydrogen chloride (3 per cent) gives a mixture of two crystalline, isomeric compounds known as methyl α- and β-D-glucosides, which do not reduce Fehling's solution and which have the

analysis of cyclic acetals. One molecule of D-glucose reacts with *one* molecule of methanol. This suggests that the sugar reacts in a ring form as illustrated (but see p. 26). The actual ring shown

cyclic acetal　　　methyl D-fructoside

was chosen tentatively by analogy with the stable γ-lactones of the aldonic acids (Tollens 1883, Fischer 1893). The formation of a ring produces a new asymmetric carbon atom (*) as shown, which explains the existence of the two isomeric forms of D-glucose and of methyl D-glucosides. Isomers that differ only in configuration at $C_{(1)}$ in aldoses or at $C_{(2)}$ in ketoses (i.e. at the reducing centre) are called *anomers*.

A *glycoside* is the name given to the product of this type obtained from a sugar by reaction with an alcohol or phenol; other examples, not necessarily prepared in the same way, are ethyl α-D-galactoside and phenyl β-L-arabinoside. In the aldosides the ring-oxygen is connected to $C_{(1)}$, whereas in the ketosides it is connected to $C_{(2)}$. In the formula above of methyl D-fructoside $C_{(5)}$ is chosen for attachment to the oxygen simply by analogy with the ring structure allotted, without experimental justification, to the methyl D-glucosides.

The methyl D-glucosides are stable to alkali, but are easily hydrolysed by dilute acids to methanol and D-glucose. The hydrolysis of methyl α-D-glucoside is catalysed by maltase, an enzyme preparation from malt extract which, however, does not affect the β-anomer. Emulsin, an enzyme preparation from bitter almonds, hydrolyses methyl β-D-glucoside but does not affect the α form (Fischer 1894). Polarimetric observations of these enzymic hydrolyses indicated that the D-glucose produced from methyl α-D-glucoside showed slight downward mutarotation, whereas that from methyl β-D-glucoside mutarotated upward. This suggests that α-D-glucose is stereochemically related to methyl α-D-glucoside, and β-D-glucose to methyl β-D-glucoside (Armstrong, 1903).

In all the D-aldoses the α-form is considered to have the hydroxyl of $C_{(1)}$ on the right of the Fischer projection formula, while in the L-series the α-isomer has the hydroxyl on the left. This was originally a convention but has now been proved by both chemical and physical methods.

Rules relating specific rotation with configuration

1. *The rules of isorotation* (Hudson 1909)

For an aldose the molecular rotation, defined as one hundredth of the product of the molecular weight and the $[\alpha]_D$, may be regarded as being made up of one part contributed by $C_{(1)}$ ($= A°$) and another part due to the rest of the molecule ($= B°$).

The α-isomer, therefore, has $[M]_D = A + B$, and the β form has $[M]_D = -A + B$. It follows that the sum of the molecular rotations ($= 2B$) is characteristic of the particular sugar and independent of the substituent on $C_{(1)}$. This is Rule I and is illustrated by the following α,β pairs:

	$[M]_D$
α-D-*glucose* penta-acetate	$+396$
β-D-*glucose* penta-acetate	$+ 15$
Therefore $2B = +411$	
methyl α-D-*glucoside* tetra-acetate	$+473$
methyl β-D-*glucoside* tetra-acetate	$- 66$
Therefore $2B = +407$	

Similarly the difference between the molecular rotations of an α,β pair ($= 2A$) is dependent solely on the group attached to $C_{(1)}$: no matter what the remainder of the molecule is, it does not affect the value. This is Rule II and is illustrated by the following pairs:

	$[M]_D$
methyl α-D-glucoside tetra-acetate	$+473$
methyl β-D-glucoside tetra-acetate	$- 66$
Therefore $2A = +539$	
methyl α-D-galactoside tetra-acetate	$+484$
methyl β-D-galactoside tetra-acetate	$- 51$
Therefore $2A = +535$	

The rules hold well in closely related structures such as the above examples, but are not of rigid universal application (Horton 1964).

2. *The lactone rule* (Hudson 1910)

The $[a]_D$ of the γ- or δ-lactone of a D-aldonic acid is positive when the hydroxyl group on $C_{(4)}$ or $C_{(5)}$ of the acid is to the right and is negative when it is to the left. This rule is illustrated by the following examples:

D-glucono-γ-lactone	D-glucono-δ-lactone	D-galactono-γ-lactone
$[a]_D + 67\cdot5°$	$[a]_D + 62\cdot0°$	$[a]_D - 70\cdot0°$

The position of the ring in monosaccharides

One of the first indications that the arbitrary allocation of a γ-oxide ring (five-membered) to the sugars was inadequate was the isolation of four distinct crystalline D-galactose penta-acetates, none of which had a free aldehyde group (Hudson 1915). The only possible explanation is that two different ring systems are present, the four isomers forming two a,β pairs. About the same time, a methyl D-glucoside was isolated (Fischer) and named methyl γ-D-glucoside to distinguish it from the known a- and β-isomers. It was not intended that the symbol 'γ' should suggest a five-membered ring, since there was no evidence to support this.

The alcohol groups of sugars are readily methylated by treatment with methyl iodide and silver oxide, or with dimethyl sulphate and sodium hydroxide solution (see p. 44 for details).

$$H - \overset{|}{\underset{|}{C}} - OH \rightarrow H - \overset{|}{\underset{|}{C}} - OMe$$

The ether groups formed are stable to acids and alkalis, whereas, as has already been mentioned, the glycosidic methyl group is readily hydrolysed by dilute acids. In this way methyl

a-D-glucoside was converted into methyl tetra-O-methyl-a-D-glucoside, which was hydrolysed to a crystalline tetra-O-methyl-D-glucose. (The -O- is inserted in the names to denote that the methyl group is joined not to the carbon skeleton of the sugar, but to an oxygen atom.) The same substance was obtained from methyl β-D-glucoside. There is ample evidence that methylation does not displace the ring in any way, and hence methyl a- and β-D-glucosides must have the same ring system. When methyl γ-D-glucoside was subjected to the same reactions a different isomeric tetra-O-methyl-D-glucose was obtained. This proves that the γ-isomer is different because of a different ring system (Irvine 1915).

Determination of the position of the ring in glycosides
Methylation method (Hirst 1923)

1. First of all the methyl glycoside is completely methylated and then hydrolysed to the tetra-O-methyl sugar in the case of the hexoses, and to the tri-O-methyl sugar in the case of the pentoses.

2. The methyl derivative is then oxidized with nitric acid under carefully controlled conditions that vary somewhat for each sugar; for example, with concentrated acid at 90° for 3 hours. The oxidation of the aldoses may be regarded as taking the following hypothetical course.

(a) The ring is broken, giving the open-chain form with an aldehyde group at $C_{(1)}$ and a secondary alcohol group at the other position previously attached to the ring oxygen.

(b) The aldehyde group is oxidized to carboxyl, and the secondary alcohol group to a carbonyl group.

(c) The carbon chain is then broken on either side of the carbonyl group, as in a normal ketone. The groups that are then terminal are converted into carboxyl groups giving two dicarboxylic acids differing in chain length by one carbon atom. If the ring is attached to both terminal carbon atoms the reaction is somewhat simpler.

(d) The ring is broken to give an aldehyde group at $C_{(1)}$ and a primary hydroxyl group at the other end of the carbon chain.

(e) Both terminal groups are oxidized to carboxyl groups. There is no chain rupture and the dicarboxylic acid has the same chain length as the original sugar derivative.

$$\begin{array}{ccccc}
\text{CHOH} & & \text{CHO} & & \text{CO}_2\text{H} \\
| & \xrightarrow{(d)} & | & \xrightarrow{(e)} & | \\
\vdots & & \vdots & & \vdots \\
| & & | & & | \\
\text{CH}_2\text{O} & & \text{CH}_2\text{OH} & & \text{CO}_2\text{H}
\end{array}$$

The following examples illustrate this general method. The easily prepared crystalline amides were often used for identifying the dicarboxylic acids produced.

Tetra-O-methyl-D-glucose, obtained from methyl α- or β-D-glucoside, gave, on treatment with nitric acid, dextro-dimethoxysuccinic acid and optically inactive D-$xylo$-trimethoxyglutaric acid (Hirst 1926). The prefix D-$xylo$- indicates that the configuration of the three methoxyl groups in this acid is the same as the hydroxyls in D-xylose.

The substituted succinic acid must have been produced by a break between $C_{(4)}$ and $C_{(5)}$ and the glutaric acid by a break between $C_{(5)}$ and $C_{(6)}$. Thus the carbonyl group, postulated in (b) above, must have been at $C_{(5)}$, so the ring oxygen in methyl α-D-glucoside is between $C_{(1)}$ and $C_{(5)}$. The ring is six-membered, and the original suggestion that it was five-membered has been disproved (see formulae on p. 29).

When tri-O-methyl-D-xylose, prepared from methyl α- or β-D-xyloside, was treated with nitric acid, a 70 per cent yield of D-$xylo$-trimethoxyglutaric acid was the only product isolated (Hirst 1923). This shows that in the original methyl D-xyloside the ring oxygen was joined to $C_{(1)}$ and $C_{(5)}$, again making a six-membered ring.

The dicarboxylic acids isolated from the oxidation of tetra-O-

CHOH
MeO— —OMe
—OMe
—O
CH_2OMe
tetra-O-methyl-
D-glucose

→

CO_2H
MeO— —OMe
—OMe
≡O
CH_2OMe
A
B

A

CO_2H
—OMe
MeO—
CO_2H
dextro-dimethoxy-
succinic acid

B

CO_2H
—OMe
MeO—
—OMe
CO_2H
D-xylo-trimethoxy-
glutaric acid

CHOH
MeO— —OMe
—OMe
CH_2O—
tri-O-methyl-D-
xylose

→

CO_2H
—OMe
MeO—
—OMe
CH_2OH

methyl-D-fructose (prepared from methyl α-D-fructoside) show that the ring is also six-membered.

By this method it may be shown that all the normal hexosides and pentosides have this same ring system of one oxygen and five carbon atoms. This has been confirmed by the use of periodate oxidation which is discussed later (p. 68).

Methylated lactones were prepared from the methyl aldosides by the sequence methylation, hydrolysis, and oxidation with bromine water. The stabilities of those prepared from methyl γ-D-glucoside, γ-D-galactoside, and γ-L-arabinoside, were compared with those obtained from the corresponding normal glycosides (Haworth 1926). By observing the $[a]_D$ of aqueous ethanolic solutions of these lactones it was possible to calculate the percentage of the lactone that had been changed to the free acid in a given time. It was found that the lactones obtained from the normal glycosides, which were known to have the δ-ring, were much less stable than the lactones from the γ-glycosides. The similarity in the stability of this latter group of lactones pointed to their all having the same ring system. Since methyl γ-D-galactoside had already been shown to have the five-membered γ-ring by use of Hudson's lactone rule (Pryde, Haworth) it was concluded that so also have methyl γ-L-arabinoside and methyl γ-D-glucoside.

Confirmation of the structure of methyl γ-D-glucoside was obtained by applying a slight modification of the methylation method (Haworth and Hirst 1927). The tetra-O-methyl-D-glucose obtained from methyl γ-D-glucoside was oxidized first with bromine water and then with nitric acid. Only dextro-dimethoxysuccinic acid was isolated (as its crystalline diamide), suggesting a break between $C_{(4)}$ and $C_{(5)}$. The ring must therefore have been attached to $C_{(4)}$ or $C_{(5)}$. The latter is ruled out because it is the position involved in the ring of normal methyl α-D-glucoside, and because no trimethoxyglutaric acid was obtained. This proves that in methyl γ-D-glucoside the ring oxygen is attached to $C_{(1)}$ and $C_{(4)}$.

Investigation of methyl γ-D-fructoside (Haworth 1927) showed that it too had a five-membered ring, the ring oxygen being attached to $C_{(2)}$ and $C_{(5)}$.

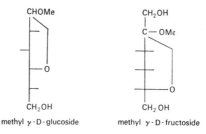

CHOMe

CH$_2$OH

O

CH$_2$OH

methyl γ-D-glucoside

CH$_2$OH

C — OMe

O

CH$_2$OH

methyl γ-D-fructoside

All normal glycosides have rings consisting of one oxygen and five carbon atoms, i.e. the ring oxygen in aldosides is joined to $C_{(1)}$ and $C_{(5)}$, and in ketosides to $C_{(2)}$ and $C_{(6)}$. The γ-glycosides all have rings of one oxygen and four carbon atoms with the ring oxygen in the γ-aldosides joined to $C_{(1)}$ and $C_{(4)}$, and in the γ-ketosides to $C_{(2)}$ and $C_{(5)}$.

The reaction of an alcohol with an aldose in the presence of hydrogen chloride is a complex one.

Equilibria between the free sugar, both anomers of the five-membered ring acetal, both anomers of the six-membered ring acetal, and probably the dialkyl acetal of the open chain form can all occur. With xylose, for example, the five-membered ring compounds are formed first, followed by slower formation of the six-membered ring derivatives. Obviously steric factors will cause variations in each of the various equilibrium positions and no two aldoses behave in exactly the same way. The action

on D-glucose of dry methanol containing 1 per cent hydrogen
chloride at room temperature leads chiefly to methyl γ-D-glu-
cosides, whereas boiling methanol containing 3 per cent hydrogen chloride gives the normal methyl D-glucosides. The
γ-aldosides are much more readily hydrolysed by dilute
aqueous acid (e.g. 0·25 per cent hydrochloric acid) than the
normal forms; this does not hold for the ketosides.

Size of the ring in the free sugars

The fact that when D-glucose (*a* or *β*) is oxidized with hypo-
bromite, D-glucono-δ-lactone is rapidly formed shows that the
sugar has a six-membered ring (Hudson 1932, Isbell 1933).
X-ray examination of some monosaccharides has shown that
their crystalline forms also have this same ring.

The normal sugar ring atoms are the same as those of pyran,
while the ring atoms of the γ-glycosides are identical with those
of furan. The sugars and their derivatives in the normal forms

pyran   furan

are, therefore, said to be *pyranose*, and the γ-forms are *furanose*
(Haworth). These names are, when necessary, used to show
which ring system is present. Crystalline aldoses are pyranoses
(e.g. D-glucopyranose), and the normal glycosides are pyranosides (e.g. methyl a-D-glucopyranoside). The γ-glycosides are
correctly named glycofuranosides: these too exist in a- and β-
forms (e.g. methyl a-D-fructofuranoside). In the rest of this
book the prefix '*γ*' will not be used for sugars or their derivatives, but will be reserved for lactones.

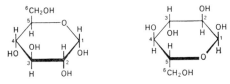

α - D - glucopyranose

Haworth proposed perspective formulae for the sugar ring,
which is represented as being in a plane at right angles to that
of the paper with the attached atoms or groups lying parallel

to the plane of the paper. The lower edge of the hexagon is directed outwards towards the reader.

β-D-Glucose is identical with the α form except for the disposition of the hydroxyl group on $C_{(1)}$: it will be noticed that the hydrogen atoms are alternately below and above the plane of the ring. The L-sugars are the mirror images of the D-forms.

By convention the ring of the D-series is usually drawn with the ring oxygen in the rear right-hand position as shown below. No convention exists for L-sugars and they are drawn either as a reflection in a mirror plane beneath the ring or in one placed on the right of the D-form. The latter will be used in this book.

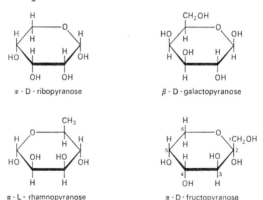

β - D - glucopyranose β - L - glucopyranose

Other examples are:

α - D - ribopyranose β - D - galactopyranose

α - L - rhamnopyranose α - D - fructopyranose

The furanose sugars and their derivatives may also be written in similar perspective formulae, for example:

methyl α-D-glucofuranoside   methyl β-D-fructofuranoside

Mutarotation

The mutarotation of an aqueous sugar solution generally follows first-order kinetics (Lowry, Hudson). There are a few sugars (e.g. L-arabinose, D-galactose, and D-fructose) whose mutarotation is more complex: this is due to an equilibrium being established between pyranose and furanose forms. The mutarotation of D-glucose is of the former type, and the α- and β-pyranoses are the predominant species. The mechanism of the reaction, which shows general acid-base catalysis, is shown below. The open-chain form is involved as an intermediate. Aldose derivatives unsubstituted at $C_{(1)}$ and ketose derivatives unsubstituted at $C_{(2)}$ generally exhibit mutarotation.

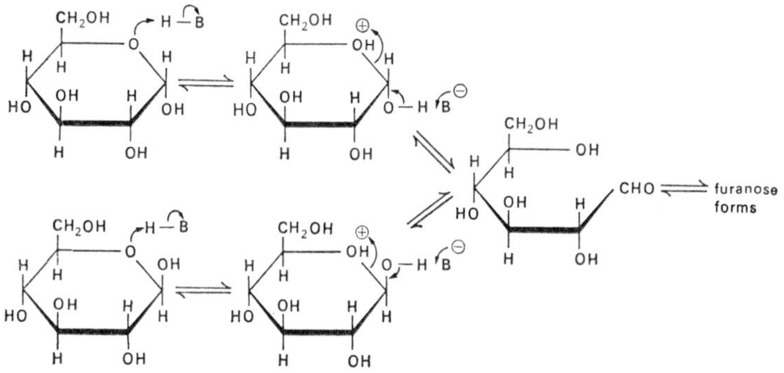

Although the concentration of the *aldehydo* form is low it is rapidly produced if the equilibrium is disturbed. Hence, the addition of a reagent, such as ethanethiol (EtSH), which reacts with the open-chain form, leads to quick and complete production of the acyclic derivative (see p. 50).

REVIEW

Methyl and phenyl glycosides of the common sugars, by J. Conchie, G. A. Levvy, and C. A. Marsh, *Adv. Carbohyd. Chem.* 1957, **12**, 157.

5

CONFORMATIONS OF
MONOSACCHARIDES

THE word 'conformation' was introduced into chemistry by Haworth in 1929, though the idea of a non-flat, puckered ring for glucose had been utilized previously by Sponsler and Dore in their work on cellulose (1926). Detailed studies of the conformations of molecules have developed extensively since about 1950.

The conformations of a molecule are the arrangements in space of the atoms of a single chemical structure (configuration); the arrangements are produced only by rotation about single bonds and are not superimposable. The various conformations of a molecule are called conformers.

Investigation of the cyclohexane molecule, which is shown with a planar ring in (1), has revealed that of the possible strainless forms the *chair* one (2) rather than a *boat* (3) is preferred. Full understanding of this topic is impossible without

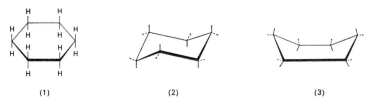

(1)   (2)   (3)

study of scale models, which show that the true shape of the ring is flatter than suggested by the illustrations. To follow further points in this chapter Catalin or Dreiding atomic models are recommended.

In the chair and boat conformer the bonds bearing substituents are either *axial* (*ax*), shown by full bonds in (2) and (3), or equatorial (*eq*), shown by dotted bonds in (2) and (3).

In a simple monosubstituted cyclohexane derivative, the two possible chair conformers (4) and (5) can rapidly interchange in solution, but the more stable form is (4) in which the substituent is equatorial to keep to a minimum the non-bonded interactions with neighbouring hydrogen atoms. In the conversion of one chair form into another the equatorial substituents become axial and vice versa. Generally the preferred conformer has the greater number of bulky groups in the equatorial positions. Exceptions to this generalization are molecules in which there are

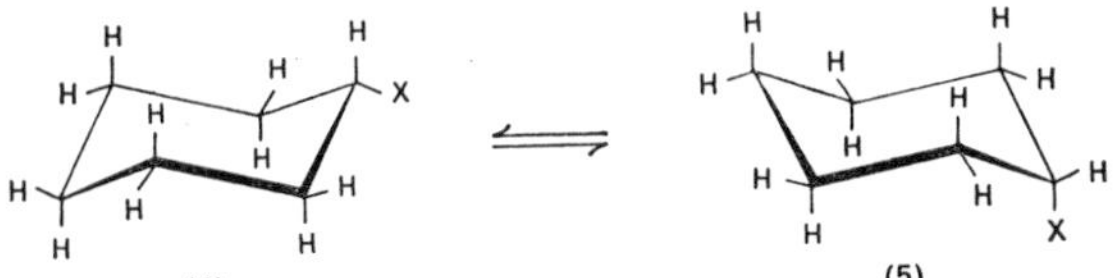

electrostatic forces. Hydrogen-bonding or dipolar interactions can cause a molecule to exist preferentially in a conformation with axial substituents. For example, 5-hydroxy-1,3-dioxan exists predominantly in the conformation with the hydroxyl group axial (6) rather than with the substituent equatorial (7) (Foster 1959).

The replacement of one carbon atom of the cyclohexane ring with an oxygen atom to give the pyranose ring does not cause any appreciable distortion of the ring and the conformational principles described for cyclohexane are applicable. Pyranose sugar rings carry many substituent groups between which non-bonded interactions are possible. Crystalline β-D-glucopyranose is (8), where all the large groups are equatorial, rather than (9), where they are axial. Other sugars have equatorial and axial

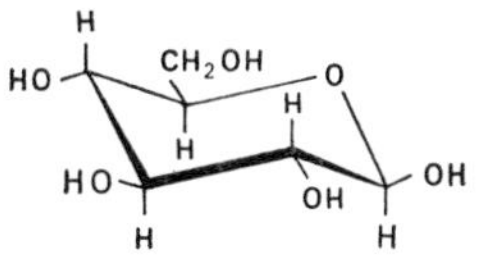

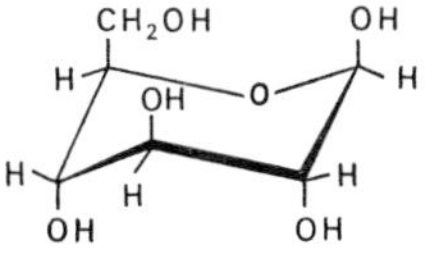

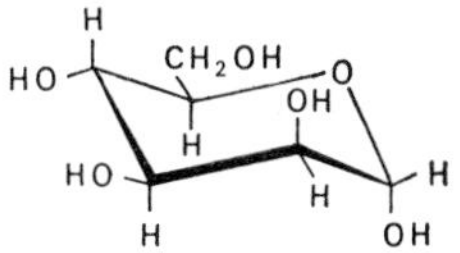

substituents in each conformer; (10) shows the preferred form of α-D-mannopyranose.

A *boat* conformation is flexible and is only one of six on a cycle of an infinite number of strainless forms. Most of these are not depictable on paper. A *twist* (or *skew boat*) form occurs half-way between each pair of boat forms. (Use of Dreiding models illustrates this point very clearly.) As shown in (11), the six ring atoms are in two groups of three, each in one plane as shown, the central atom of each group being in the plane of the other group. An attempt to draw (11) in perspective is shown in (12).

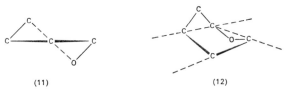

(11)   (12)

The *half-chair* conformation has to be considered when a six-membered ring contains either a double bond (13), or an epoxide ring (14), causing four adjacent atoms to be in one plane.

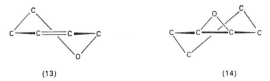

(13)   (14)

When considering part of a molecule of a conformation for stereochemical purposes, the projected angle between groups on adjacent ring atoms is important. This is the angle between groups when viewed along the bond joining them, as in (15). A

(15)

circle is drawn in the projection diagram to represent the bond joining the two ring atoms (Newman projection).

It is important to know which conformer is preferred for a given sugar, because the arrangement of hydroxyl groups, which will influence the course and rate of reactions, will be different in the two chair forms. Nevertheless, in some cases, a molecule can react in a less preferred conformer (see, for example, p. 59).

Nomenclature of sugar conformers

There is no internationally agreed nomenclature system for sugar conformers. The original system, due to Reeves (1946), is inadequate for some purposes, and other systems have been proposed (Guthrie 1958, Isbell and Tipson 1959). Reeves defines the ring shapes of chair forms of the pyranose ring, without reference to substituents, as shown in (16) and (17). When

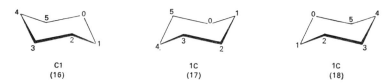

| C1 | 1C | 1C |
| (16) | (17) | (18) |

the ring shape (17) is turned over through 180° it gives (18), which is the mirror image of (16). Therefore, the D- and L-forms of a sugar in the *same* conformation (that is with the same axial-equatorial arrangement of groups) have different symbols; C1 and 1C must, therefore, always be prefixed by D- or L-, otherwise they are without meaning.

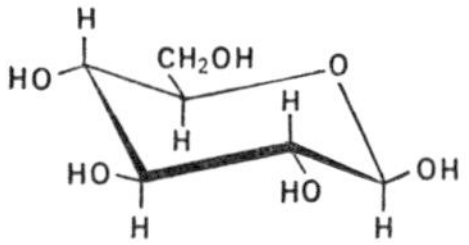

β-D-glucose-C1 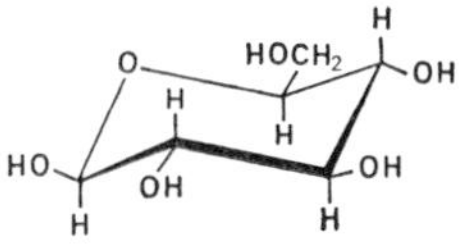   β-L-glucose-1C

In this book, conformations will be named using Isbell and Tipson's system, but, in every case, the corresponding Reeves' symbol will be given in parentheses. Isbell and Tipson use the position of the anomeric substituent (on $C_{(1)}$ in aldoses, on $C_{(2)}$ in ketoses) in α anomers as reference, as shown below. In a β-anomer, the corresponding α-anomer is used to name the ring

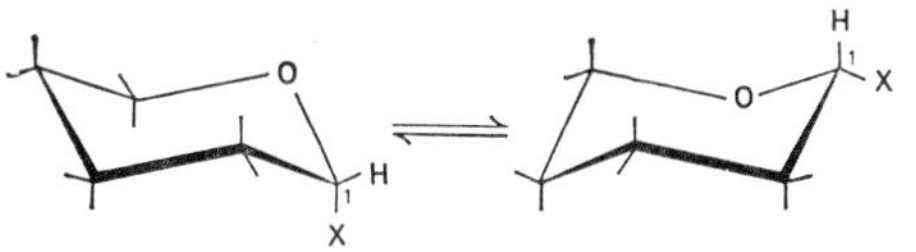

CA (D-C1)   CE (D-1C) 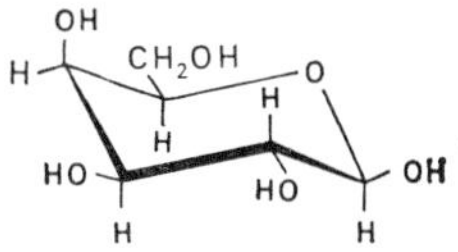   β-D-galactopyranose
                                         CA (D-C1)

C=chair; A = axial; E = equatorial

shape as in β-D-galactopyranose where the α-anomer would have the hydroxyl group in the axial position.

The six possible boat conformations of the pyranose ring are named by using the position of the glycosidic substituent in the α-anomer and the number of one of the two ring atoms not in the plane of the other four. For example:

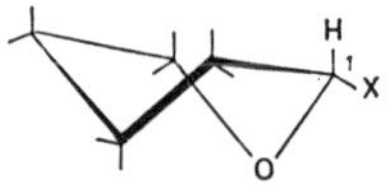

B_3E (D-3B) 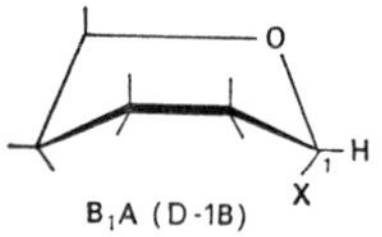 B_1A (D-1B)

Determination of conformation

Cuprammonium forms complexes with vicinal diols only if the projected angle between the adjacent hydroxyl groups is $0°$ or $\pm 60°$ (Reeves 1946). Now projected angles of $0°$ only occur in the boat form but angles of $\pm 60°$ occur between ax–eq or eq–eq diols of a chair conformer. Using this method Reeves was able to show that chairs were preferred to boats, and also to decide which of the two chair forms was preferred. The method has recently been extended to vicinal amino-alcohols.

Attempts have been made to determine preferred conformers by assigning arbitrary numerical factors to various stereochemical features, and then summing these for the possible conformations of a molecule (Reeves). Such methods involve oversimplification. Infrared and proton magnetic resonance spectrometries as well as X-ray studies have been used success-

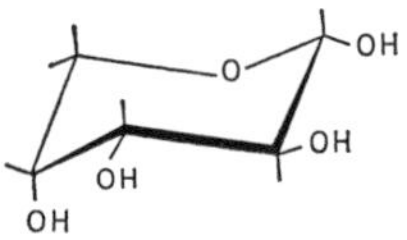

α-D-arabinose
CE (D-1C)

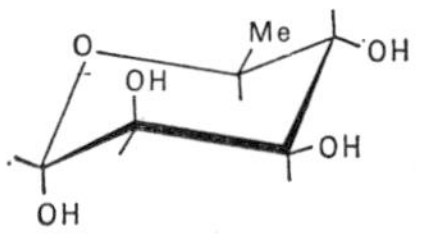

α-L-rhamnose
CA (L-1C)

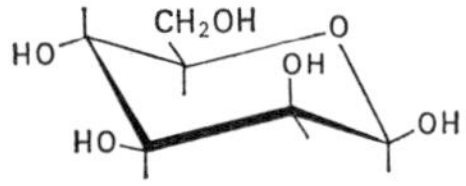

β-D-mannose
CA (D-C1)

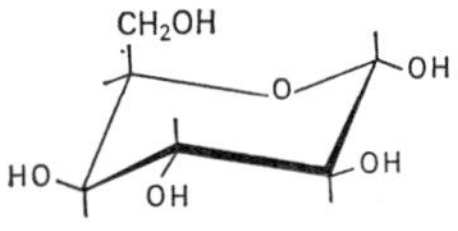

α-D-idose
CE (D-1C)

fully to determine the preferred conformations of sugar molecules.

The preferred conformations of a few sugars are shown on the previous page.

The easiest way of converting a Haworth or Fischer formula into the corresponding CA (D-C1) chair formula is shown below. It should be noted that the substituents are alternately axial and equatorial, starting with alpha-axial, which is easily remembered. It is also a help to remember that in this conformation, β-D-glucose has every substituent equatorial.

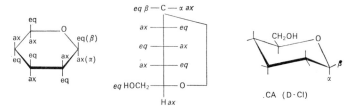

The five-membered furanose ring exists as a slightly puckered, almost planar ring. It is possible, therefore, to have adjacent hydroxyl groups truly *cis* with a projected angle of 0°.

Consideration of the conformation of sugar molecules has helped greatly in understanding their reactions. Examples will be found in the succeeding pages.

REVIEWS

Principles of conformational analysis, by D. H. R. Barton and R. C. Cookson, *Q. Rev. chem. Soc.* 1956, **10**, 44.

Newer aspects of the stereochemistry of carbohydrates, by R. J. Ferrier and W. G. Overend, *Q. Rev. chem. Soc.* 1959, **13**, 265.

Cuprammonium–glycoside complexes, by R. E. Reeves, *Adv. Carbohyd. Chem.* 1951, **6**, 107.

Conformational analysis in carbohydrate chemistry, by S. J. Angyal, Chapter 6 in *Conformational analysis* (Wiley, 1966).

Conformational analysis of organic compounds, by J. McKenna, *Royal Institute of Chemistry, Lecture Series*, 1966, No. 1.

6

ACTION OF ACIDS AND ALKALIS ON MONOSACCHARIDES

Acids

EXTREMELY dilute aqueous solutions of acids catalyse interchange between the various anomeric and ring forms of monosaccharides. Dilute solutions of acids in anhydrous alcohols convert the monosaccharides into glycosides (see p. 23). In dilute aqueous solutions an equilibrium is set up between aldohexoses and the 1,6-anhydro-sugars (see p. 64). For this reaction the aldohexose must be in the β-form of the CE(D-1C or L-C1) conformation so that the groups at $C_{(1)}$ and $C_{(6)}$ are both axial. The percentage yields of 1,6-anhydro-aldohexoses

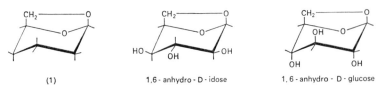

(1)   1,6 - anhydro - D - idose   1, 6 - anhydro - D - glucose

are shown in the table (Richtmyer 1958). The figures show that sugars such as D-idose and D-altrose in which the CE (D-1C) conformation is preferred form good yields of 1,6-anhydro

D-Hexose	Anhydrosugar	D-Hexose	Anhydrosugar
idose	75	talose	12
altrose	57	galactose	1·7
gulose	43	mannose	0·6
allose	14	glucose	0·3

derivatives. Aldoses that exist preferentially in the CA (D-C1) conformer, such as D-glucose and D-mannose, yield little anhydro compound. The presence of bulky substituents in the axial positions of 1,6-anhydro-D-glucose should be noted.

In addition to promoting the formation of the 1,6-anhydro

compound, the action of hot dilute aqueous acids on aldoses
can yield di-, tri-, and oligo-saccharides by elimination of water
between the anomeric hydroxyl group of one aldose molecule
and a hydroxyl group in a second molecule (see Chapter 13).
This process is called reversion. The disaccharides from aldohexoses generally contain the $C_{(1)} \rightarrow C_{(6)}$ link; thus D-glucose
yields isomaltose and gentiobiose (see also p. 103), but other
isomeric disaccharides are also produced.

Hot moderately concentrated acids (e.g. 12 per cent hydrochloric acid) cause more extensive dehydration. Aldopentoses
(2; R = H) are converted into furfuraldehyde (3; R = H), and
aldohexoses (2; R = CH_2OH) into 5-hydroxymethylfurfural-
dehyde (3; R = CH_2OH). Stronger acids cause the formation of
tarry polymeric substances.

$$\begin{array}{ccc}
\text{CHOH—CHOH} & & \text{CH——CH} \\
| \quad\quad\; | & & \;\| \quad\;\; \| \\
\text{R—CHOH} \;\; \text{CHOH—CHO} & \rightarrow & \text{R—C} \quad\;\; \text{C—CHO} \\
& & \text{O} \\
\text{(2)} & & \text{(3)}
\end{array}$$

Alkalis

Epimerizations brought about by heating in aqueous pyridine have already been mentioned (pp. 15, 18).

Even in mild alkali, such as saturated lime water at room
temperature, sugars are rapidly converted into mixtures (the
Lobry de Bruyn–Alberda van Ekenstein rearrangement). Thus
D-glucose gives a mixture of D-mannose, D-fructose, and unchanged sugar, formed via a 1,2-enediol intermediate as shown
in the partial formulae. For example, when treated with 0·04 per
cent sodium hydroxide, D-glucose yields D-fructose (about 30
per cent), D-mannose (1 per cent), and unchanged D-glucose

$$\begin{array}{ccccc}
\text{CHO} & & \text{CHOH} & & \text{CHO} \\
| & & \| & & | \\
\text{HCOH} & \rightleftharpoons & \text{COH} & \rightleftharpoons & \text{HOCH} \\
| & & | & & | \\
\text{HOCH} & & \text{HOCH} & & \text{HOCH} \\
\text{D-glucose} & & \text{1,2-enediol} & & \text{D-mannose}
\end{array}$$

$$\updownarrow$$

$$\begin{array}{ccccc}
\text{CH}_2\text{OH} & & \text{CH}_2\text{OH} & & \text{CH}_2\text{OH} \\
| & & | & & | \\
\text{CO} & \rightleftharpoons & \text{COH} & \rightleftharpoons & \text{CO} \\
| & & \| & & | \\
\text{HOCH} & & \text{HOC} & & \text{HCOH} \\
\text{D-fructose} & & \text{2,3-enediol} & & \text{D-allulose}
\end{array}$$

(66 per cent) (Sowden 1952). A small amount of D-allulose may also be formed under some conditions via the 2,3-enediol. This mechanism accounts for the equilibrium between the D-glucose and D-mannose derivatives obtained when dilute alkali is added to 2,3,4,6-tetra-O-methyl-D-glucose; in this case no ketose can be produced.

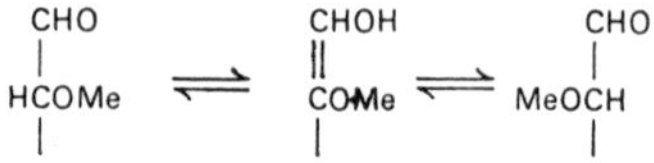

$$
\begin{array}{ccc}
\text{CHO} & \text{CHOH} & \text{CHO} \\
| & \| & | \\
\text{HCOMe} & \text{COMe} & \text{MeOCH} \\
| & | & |
\end{array}
$$

With longer reaction times, high concentration or greater excesses of alkali, or by heating, a more complex mixture of products is produced, including iso- and meta-saccharinic acids. The latter may be obtained in good yield (Kenner 1954), and have been used in the synthesis of 2-deoxy-D-ribose (p. 85). These rearrangements involve a β-alkoxycarbonyl elimination, followed by a benzilic acid rearrangement [RCO·CO·R' → RR'C(OH)CO$_2$H]. A hydroxyl or alkoxyl group (-O-alkyl or -O-monosaccharide) in the β-position with respect to an actual or potential carbonyl group is very labile and may be eliminated by alkali. An alkoxyl group is lost more readily than a hydroxyl. 3-O-Substituted-hexoses yield metasaccharinic acid as shown below.

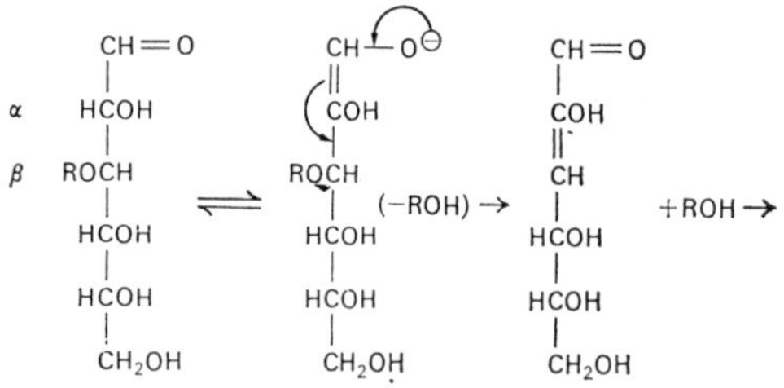

$$
\begin{array}{cccc}
& \text{CH}=\text{O} & \text{CH}\!-\!\text{O}^{\ominus} & \text{CH}=\text{O} \\
& | & \| & | \\
\alpha & \text{HCOH} & \text{COH} & \text{COH} \\
& | & | & \| \\
\beta & \text{ROCH} & \text{RQCH} & \text{CH} \\
& | \rightleftharpoons & | \;\;(-\text{ROH}) \rightarrow & | \;\;+\text{ROH} \rightarrow \\
& \text{HCOH} & \text{HCOH} & \text{HCOH} \\
& | & | & | \\
& \text{HCOH} & \text{HCOH} & \text{HCOH} \\
& | & | & | \\
& \text{CH}_2\text{OH} & \text{CH}_2\text{OH} & \text{CH}_2\text{OH}
\end{array}
$$

e. g. 3-O-methyl-D-glucose (R=CH$_3$)
or laminaribiose (R=β-D-glucopyranosyl)

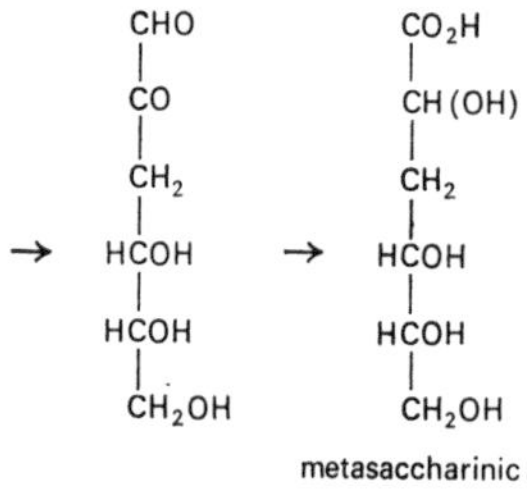

$$
\begin{array}{cc}
\text{CHO} & \text{CO}_2\text{H} \\
| & | \\
\text{CO} & \text{CH(OH)} \\
| & | \\
\text{CH}_2 & \text{CH}_2 \\
\rightarrow \;\; | & \rightarrow \;\; | \\
\text{HCOH} & \text{HCOH} \\
| & | \\
\text{HCOH} & \text{HCOH} \\
| & | \\
\text{CH}_2\text{OH} & \text{CH}_2\text{OH}
\end{array}
$$

metasaccharinic acid

4-*O*-Substituted-hexoses react to give isosaccharinic acid, as follows:

```
      CHO                 CH₂OH                CH₂OH
       |                   |                    |
     ·HCOH                 C=O                  C↙O⊖
       |                   |                    ‖
     HOCH      ⇌         HOCH       ⇌         HOC
       |                   |                    ↙
     HCOR                HCOR                 HCOR
       |                   |                    ↗
     HCOH                HCOH                 HCOH
       |                   |                    |
     ·CH₂OH               CH₂OH                CH₂OH
```

e.g. 4-*O*-methyl-D-glucose (R=CH₃),
cellobiose (R=β-D-glucopyranosyl),
or maltose (R=α-D-glucopyranosyl)

```
     CH₂OH              ·CH₂OH                CO₂H
      |                   |                    |
      C=O                 CO                  C(OH)CH₂OH
      |                   |                    |
     HOC                  CO                  CH₂
      ‖                   |                    |
 →    CH        →        CH₂         →        HCOH
      |                   |                    |
     HCOH                HCOH                 CH₂OH
      |                   |
     CH₂OH               CH₂OH              isosaccharinic acid
```

A sugar unit eliminated in these transformations is then subjected to further attack by the alkali present.

REVIEWS

Formation of furan compounds from hexoses, by F. H. Newth, *Adv. Carbohyd. Chem.* 1951, **6**, 83.

Alkaline degradation of polysaccharides, by R. L. Whistler and J. M. BeMiller, *Adv. Carbohyd. Chem.* 1958, **13**, 289.

The Lobry de Bruyn–Alberda van Ekenstein transformation, by J. C. Speck, jr., *Adv. Carbohyd. Chem.* 1958, **13**, 63.

7

ETHERS AND ACETALS

Ethers

THE *methyl ethers* are the commonest derivatives of this type. One method for their preparation (Purdie and Irvine 1903) is to boil the sugar derivative under reflux with methyl iodide in the presence of silver oxide.

$$-\overset{|}{\underset{|}{C}}-OH + MeI \longrightarrow -\overset{|}{\underset{|}{C}}-OMe + HI$$

$$2HI + Ag_2O \longrightarrow 2AgI + H_2O$$

The method, although mild, is not suitable for free sugars because of the oxidizing action of silver oxide.

In general, several treatments are necessary before complete substitution is achieved, though one treatment may be enough if N,N-dimethylformamide is added (R. Kuhn 1955). Even more effective is a mixture of methyl iodide, dimethylformamide, and both the oxide and the hydroxide of either barium or strontium (R. Kuhn 1961).

A second methylation method, which was first used in the carbohydrate field for cellulose (Denham 1913) and shown to be generally applicable (Haworth 1915), consists of adding gradually, to the substance to be methylated, equivalent quantities of aqueous sodium hydroxide and dimethyl sulphate. About three times the theoretical amount of the reagents are used.

$$-\overset{|}{\underset{|}{C}}-OH + Me_2SO_4 + NaOH \longrightarrow -\overset{|}{\underset{|}{C}}-OMe + MeNaSO_4 + H_2O$$

Two other methods less frequently used involve addition of methyl iodide to the sugar derivative that has been treated with thallous hydroxide, or with sodium in liquid ammonia.

$$-\overset{|}{\underset{|}{C}}-OH \overset{Na}{\longrightarrow} -\overset{|}{\underset{|}{C}}-ONa \overset{MeI}{\longrightarrow} -\overset{|}{\underset{|}{C}}-OMe + NaI$$

Methyl derivatives, being more volatile than the corresponding alcohol, are often readily purified by high vacuum distillation. No ring shift takes place on methylation and the methyl groups do not migrate (see p. 26). Methyl groups are very stable and are resistant to acid and alkali but they can be removed with boron trichloride (Bourne 1958). The methoxyl content of a substance is estimated quantitatively by heating it with constant-boiling hydriodic acid (Zeisel). Methyl iodide is produced and may be determined either by conversion into silver iodide, or by titrimetry.

Recent work has shown that methyl and other alkyl ethers may be prepared by reacting the carbohydrate derivative with sodium hydride in an aprotic solvent, such as N,N-dimethylformamide or dimethyl sulphoxide, followed by the addition of the alkyl bromide.

Trimethylsilyl ethers. These derivatives of carbohydrates are frequently used in gas-liquid chromatography (see p. 132) because they are much more volatile than the parent alcohols. A number of silylating agents is available; among the best is a mixture of hexamethyldisilazane ($Me_3SiNHSiMe_3$) and trimethylchlorosilane (Me_3SiCl) in pyridine (Sweeley 1963). Bistrimethylsilylacetamide [$CH_3C(OSiMe_3)$=$NSiMe_3$] is also a powerful trimethylsilylating agent. If necessary the parent alcohol can be recovered by refluxing the trimethylsilyl ether in 50 per cent aqueous methanol.

Benzyl ethers may be prepared by treating the sugar derivative with benzyl chloride in the presence of aqueous sodium hydroxide or of silver oxide and dimethylformamide. The stability of benzyl ethers is similar to that of methyl ethers except that debenzylation is easily achieved by catalytic hydrogenation.

$$-\overset{|}{\underset{|}{C}}-OCH_2C_6H_5 \quad \overset{H_2}{\rightarrow} \quad -\overset{|}{\underset{|}{C}}-OH + C_6H_5CH_3$$

benzyl ether toluene

Triphenylmethyl (or 'trityl') *ethers* are obtained by treating sugars with triphenylmethyl chloride in pyridine solution. This reaction is interesting because the primary hydroxyl group reacts preferentially (Helferich 1924). For example:

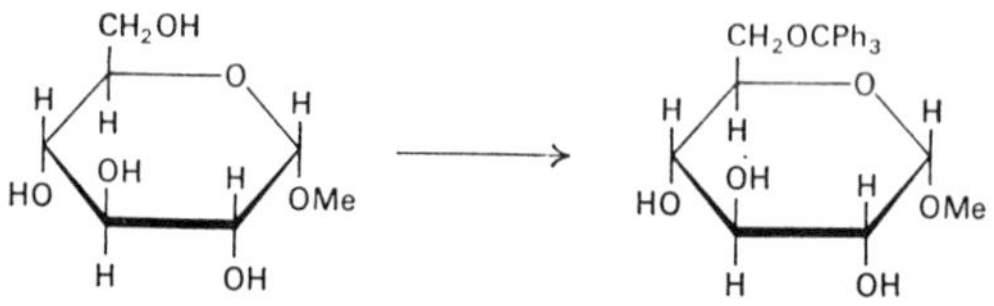

methyl α-D-glucoside

methyl 6-O-triphenyl-methyl-α-D-glucoside

However, secondary alcohol groups will also react, but more slowly.

Triphenylmethyl groups are rapidly and quantitatively removed at room temperature with a saturated solution of hydrogen bromide in glacial acetic acid.

$$CH_2OCPh_3 + HBr \rightarrow CH_2OH + Ph_3CBr$$
triphenylmethyl
bromide

Acetals

Monosaccharides and certain of their derivatives react with aldehydes and ketones in the presence of a dehydrating agent such as sulphuric acid, zinc chloride, or phosphorus pentoxide to give cyclic acetals (Fischer 1895).

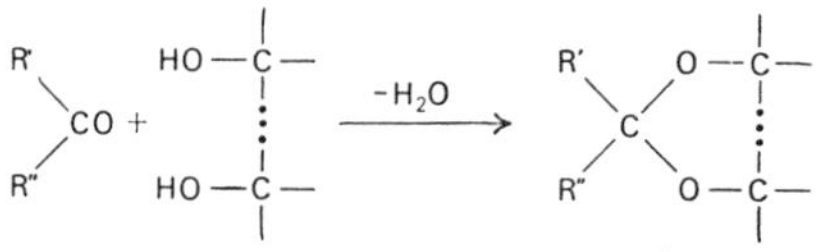

acetal

The products obtained are often crystalline and serve as convenient intermediates in syntheses. They are stable to alkali, but the aldehyde or ketone residue is readily removed by dilute acid.

D-Glucose reacts at room temperature with acetone containing sulphuric acid to give crystalline di-O-isopropylidene-D-glucose (also called 'diacetone glucose'). In addition, a smaller amount of a crystalline mono-O-isopropylidene derivative is obtained which is also isolated in excellent yield by the partial hydrolysis of the di-O-isopropylidene derivative. More drastic hydrolysis of either derivative leads to D-glucose.

The position of the isopropylidene groups may be established as follows.

(a) Neither di- nor mono-O-isopropylidene-D-glucose reduces Fehling's solution. This shows that in both compounds $C_{(1)}$ is substituted.

(b) Methylation of di-O-isopropylidene-D-glucose gives a mono-methyl ether from which the acetone residues may be removed to leave a mono-O-methyl-D-glucose, which readily gives a mono-O-methyl-D-glucosazone. This shows that the mono-O-methyl glucose has free hydroxyl groups on $C_{(1)}$ and $C_{(2)}$, i.e. in di-O-isopropylidene-D-glucose the hydroxyls on $C_{(1)}$ and $C_{(2)}$ are substituted.

(c) Similarly, mono-O-isopropylidene-D-glucose leads to a tri-O-methyl-D-glucose, which gives a tri-O-methyl-D-glucosazone. This proves that the acetone residue in mono-O-isopropylidene-D-glucose is on $C_{(1)}$ and $C_{(2)}$. Because of the smoothness of

$$
\begin{array}{l}
\text{CHO} \quad\quad \text{Me} \\
| \quad\quad\quad\quad\;\; >\!\!C\!\!< \\
\text{HCO} \quad\quad\quad \text{Me} \quad O \\
| \quad\quad\quad\quad\quad\quad\;\; |
\end{array}
$$

the conversion of the di- to the mono-O-isopropylidene derivative, it follows that one acetone residue in the former compound is also on $C_{(1)}$ and $C_{(2)}$.

(d) The tri-O-methyl-glucose above may be further converted into syrupy 2,3,5,6-tetra-O-methyl-D-glucofuranose. This shows that the acetone derivatives contain a furanose ring.

(e) The mono-O-methyl-D-glucose obtained above is oxidized with nitric acid to a mono-O-methyl-D-glucosaccharonolactone, which shows that the mono-O-methyl-glucose had a free hydroxyl on $C_{(6)}$. The second acetone residue is therefore attached to $C_{(3)}$ and $C_{(6)}$ or to $C_{(5)}$ and $C_{(6)}$.

(f) Treatment of the mono-O-methyl-D-glucose with hydrogen cyanide followed by hydrolysis gives a mono-O-methyl-D-glucoheptonolactone. This lactone is rapidly hydrolysed and is

1,2-O-isopropylidene-D-glucofuranose

1,2:5,6-di-O-isopropylidene-D-glucofuranose

therefore a δ-lactone. The stable γ-form cannot be obtained. It follows that in this lactone the methyl group is γ to the carbonyl group. This means that the mono-O-methyl-glucose is 3-O-methyl-D-glucose and that in di-O-isopropylidene-D-glucose $C_{(3)}$ has a free hydroxyl group.

It has thus been shown that the two acetone derivatives of D-glucose are 1,2-O-isopropylidene-D-glucofuranose and 1,2 : 5,6-di-O-isopropylidene-D-glucofuranose.

By similar methods the structures of acetone derivatives of other sugars have been proved. These include 2,3 : 5,6-di-O-isopropylidene-D-mannofuranose, 1,2 : 3,4-di-O-isopropylidene-D-galactopyranose, 2,3 : 4,6-di-O-isopropylidene-L-sorbofuranose, and 1,2 : 4,5- and 2,3 : 4,5-di-O-isopropylidene-D-fructopyranose.

Generally the hydroxyl groups involved are vicinal and *cis*, though this is not necessary if a primary hydroxyl group is involved. Many di-O-isopropylidene derivatives from furanose sugars give, on mild hydrolysis, the corresponding mono-O-isopropylidene compound with two fused five-membered rings.

(1)   (2)   (3)

Formula (1) is 1,2-O-isopropylidene-D-glucose. Interaction is possible between large *endo* substituents. Formula (2) shows an end-on view of two fused five-membered rings. In those derivatives where two fused five-membered ring systems are possible, that with minimum number of *endo* substituents will be formed. D-Ribose, for example, could form three acetone derivatives: the 1,2-α- and the 2,3-α- and 2,3-β-D-ribofuranose compounds. The last (3) has only one *endo* substituent (a methyl group) and is the compound found in practice. When a five-membered ring is fused to a six-membered pyranose ring, distortions will be brought about in the latter due to the planar five-membered ring. Again the hydroxyls involved are vicinal and *cis* as in the D-galactose derivative mentioned above.

The derivatives of aldehydes usually have a six-membered acetal ring fused to a six-membered pyranose ring. Condensation generally occurs on $C_{(4)}$ and $C_{(6)}$ in hexose derivatives. Thus D-glucose and methyl α-D-glucopyranoside, when treated with benzaldehyde in the presence of zinc chloride, give the 4,6-O-benzylidene derivatives. Although, theoretically, two isomers should result because of the introduction of a new asymmetric carbon atom (*), in practice only one is obtained by this method. This has the large phenyl group in the equatorial position as shown.

methyl 4,6-O-benzylidene-α-D-glucoside

The 4,6-acetals of hexoses may have either *trans*- or *cis*-fused ring systems. The methyl D-glucoside derivative shown has *trans*-fused rings; that is, the aldehyde has reacted with a *trans* pair of hydroxyls. The ring junction is rigid because the ring junction bonds from the pyranose ring, *trans* (*eq–eq*), would have to take up the sterically impossible *trans* (*ax–ax*) position in the alternative chair conformation. This rigidity at the ring junction does not prevent flexibility at the other end of the pyranose ring (see, for example, p. 59).

'O-inside'   'H-inside'
(pyranose ring CA)   (pyranose ring CE)
methyl 4,6-O-benzylidene-α-D-galactopyranoside

For *cis* (*ax–eq*) fused rings two isomeric products are possible, each derived from one of the two possible chair conformations of the hexopyranose ring, e.g. methyl 4,6-O-benzylidene-α-D-galactopyranoside.

The phenyl group is assumed to be in the preferred equatorial position in both isomers. There is less non-bonded interaction in the 'O-inside' isomer and this is probably preferred. It must be understood that the above possible products are *isomers*. The 'O-inside' isomer may also exist in an 'H-inside' conformation, and vice versa, but they will then have the phenyl group axial.

Acetaldehyde reacts similarly to benzaldehyde to form ethylidene acetals.

Acetals are useful blocking groups in carbohydrate syntheses, because they are stable to alkali but readily removed by dilute acids or ion-exchange resins of the acid type.

Thioacetals

It has been described in Chapter 4 how sugars react with alcohols to give cyclic derivatives. However, with thiols (mercaptans) such as ethanethiol, EtSH, in the presence of concentrated hydrochloric acid, aldoses react as aldehydes to give

CHO	CH(SEt)$_2$	CH(SEt)$_2$	CHO
		OMe	OMe
		MeO	MeO
		OMe	OMe
		OMe	OMe
CH$_2$OH	CH$_2$OH	CH$_2$OMe	CH$_2$OMe
D-glucose	D-glucose diethyl dithioacetal	penta-O-methyl-D-glucose diethyl dithioacetal	penta-O-methyl-aldehydo-D-glucose

HOCH$_2$
HO — H   O
OH   H   H, OMe
H   OH

methyl D-glucofuranoside

thioacetals (mercaptals), which have an acyclic structure. The structure of the product is proved by methylation, followed by removal of the mercaptal group with aqueous mercuric chloride, to give a penta-O-methyl-aldehydo-D-glucose, isomeric with the methyl tetra-O-methyl-D-glucosides mentioned previously. The presence of the free aldehyde group may be detected with Schiff's reagent, which is immediately coloured, and by the ready formation of a semicarbazone without loss of a methyl group.

If a mercaptal is shaken with methanol in the presence of mercuric chloride and oxide, methyl α- and β-furanosides are obtained. This is the best general method for preparing aldofuranosides. The use of these thioacetals in the degradation of sugars (p. 19) has already been mentioned. Thioacetals of ketoses are not obtained directly.

REVIEWS

Benzyl ethers of sugars, by C. M. McCloskey, *Adv. Carbohyd. Chem.* 1957, **12**, 137.

Trityl ethers of carbohydrates, by B. Helferich, *Adv. Carbohyd. Chem.* 1948, **3**, 79.

Stereochemistry of cyclic derivatives of carbohydrates, by J. Mills, *Adv. Carbohyd. Chem.* 1955, **10**, 1.

Cyclic acetals of the aldoses and aldosides, by A. N. de Belder, *Adv. Carbohyd. Chem.* 1965, **20**, 220.

8

ESTERS AND ANHYDRO SUGARS

ESTERS

THE hydroxyl groups of sugars and their derivatives may be esterified by many of the normal processes. Use of excess of reagents results in the expected product in which all of the free hydroxyl groups have been esterified. Partial esterification can be achieved by using a deficiency of reagent: primary hydroxyl groups are the most reactive, but the order of reactivity amongst secondary hydroxyl groups is not yet fully understood. For example, partial benzoylation of methyl α-D-glucopyranoside yields mainly the 2,6-diester, whereas the 3,6-diester is obtained from the β-D-glucoside.

Esters are readily hydrolysed by alkalis (though not always to the parent alcohol), but are somewhat more stable to acids.

Carbonates

Either cyclic or acyclic carbonate groups may be formed, depending on the reagent used and the structure of the compound being esterified.

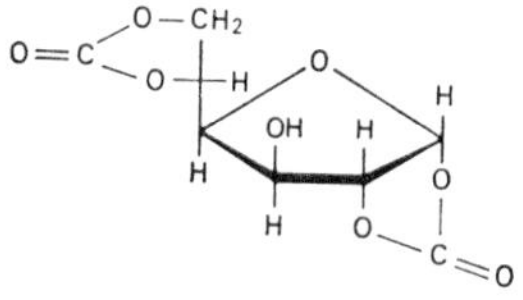

D-glucose
1,2:5,6-dicarbonate

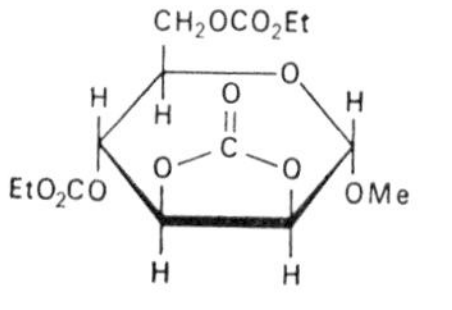

methyl 4,6-di-O-ethoxycarbonyl-
α-D-mannoside 2,3 carbonate

When a sugar is treated with carbonyl chloride (phosgene) in pyridine at or below room temperature, the ester, isolated by adding water, contains only cyclic carbonate groups. These occupy the same positions as the isopropylidene groups of the corresponding acetone derivatives (p. 46). D-Glucose, for example, gives D-glucose 1,2 : 5,6-dicarbonate. In contrast to the isopropylidene group, the carbonate group is stable to acid, but easily hydrolysed by alkali. Partial hydrolysis of D-glucose

1,2 : 5,6-dicarbonate gives D-glucose 5,6-carbonate (cf. the iso-propylidene compound). Pure crystalline aldofuranosides have been prepared using carbonates as intermediates (Haworth 1929). For example, 1,2-O-isopropylidene-D-glucose with phosgene in pyridine gives the 5,6-carbonate which, on treatment with methanolic hydrogen chloride, gives a mixture of methyl α- and β-D-glucoside 5,6-carbonates from which the α-form is obtained by crystallization. Alkaline hydrolysis gives pure crystalline methyl α-D-glucofuranoside.

Reaction of a sugar with an alkyl chloroformate in the presence of aqueous sodium hydroxide gives derivatives with cyclic and acyclic carbonate groups. The cyclic groups are formed wherever possible. Thus methyl α-D-mannopyranoside and ethyl chloroformate give methyl 4,6-d-O-ethoxycarbonyl-α-D-mannoside 2,3-carbonate.

Acetates

Acetylation of all free hydroxyl groups in an aldose is achieved by heating the substance with acetic anhydride in the presence of sodium acetate, zinc chloride, sulphuric acid, or perchloric acid, or by dissolving the substance in pyridine and acetic anhydride. The product is usually isolated by pouring the reaction mixture into a large excess of water. When the hydroxyl on $C_{(1)}$ is acetylated, either the α- or the β-anomer may be produced. The directive influence of the catalyst is important; D-glucose with acetic anhydride in the presence of zinc chloride gives α-D-glucopyranose penta-acetate, whereas with sodium acetate the β-anomer is formed. Furthermore the β-anomer, on being heated in acetic anhydride containing zinc chloride, is converted into the α-form.

β-D-glucopyranose penta-acetate   D-glucose   α-D-glucopyranose penta-acetate

Deacetylation is normally accomplished with aqueous alkali or, better, catalytically with sodium methoxide in methanol. Methanolic ammonia is also used.

$$\text{HCOOCMe} \xrightarrow[\text{MeOH}]{\text{MeONa}} \text{HCOH} + \text{MeCO}_2\text{Me}$$

methyl
acetate

The acetoxy group on $C_{(1)}$ can be replaced with a bromine atom by treating the acetate with cold glacial acetic acid saturated with hydrogen bromide. For example, an α- or β-hexose penta-acetate reacts to give the α-hexosyl bromide tetra-acetate, commonly called acetobromohexose. The reactivity of this atom is exploited in the synthesis of $C_{(1)}$ derivatives. For example, treatment of the acetobromo sugar with an alcohol in the presence of silver carbonate is a general method for preparing β-glycosides (Koenigs and Knorr 1901). A better yield is obtained by using silver oxide, anhydrous calcium sulphate, and iodide (Evans 1938), or zinc acetate (Helferich 1949) in place of silver carbonate. In some cases the corresponding α-anomer is obtained when mercuric acetate is substituted for silver carbonate (Zemplen 1929).

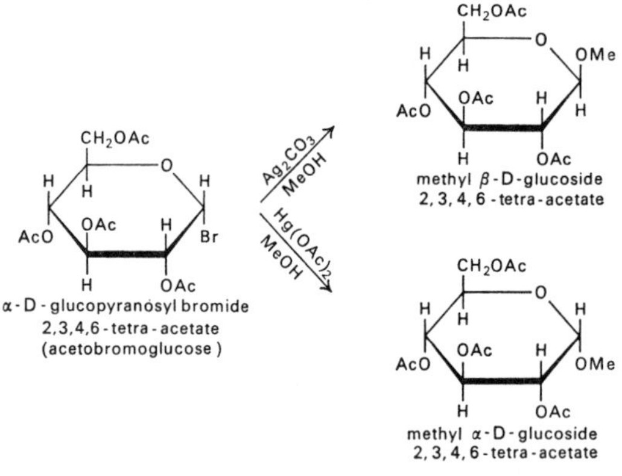

α-D-glucopyranosyl bromide
2,3,4,6-tetra-acetate
(acetobromoglucose)

methyl β-D-glucoside
2,3,4,6-tetra-acetate

methyl α-D-glucoside
2,3,4,6-tetra-acetate

Most naturally occurring glycosides are β-D-glucopyranosides. This is shown by their hydrolysis by emulsin and by the isolation of 2,3,4,6-tetra-O-methyl-D-glucose after methylation and hydrolysis. The non-sugar portion, known as the aglycone (aglucone when the substance is a glucoside), is an alcohol or a phenol. The glucoside, salicin, obtained from the willow (*Salix*) is (*o*-hydroxymethyl)-phenyl-β-D-glucoside. The methods already described have been adapted for synthesizing such naturally-occurring glucosides.

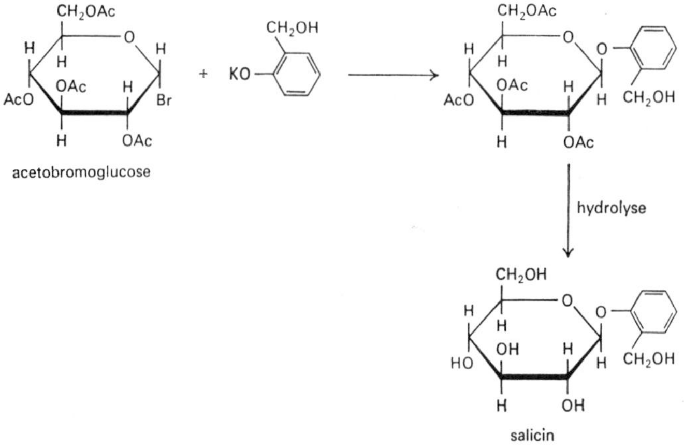

acetobromoglucose

hydrolyse

salicin

The glycosides are widely distributed in nature and include the anthocyanins (plant colouring matters). If the aglycone is replaced by another sugar molecule, the glycoside is then a disaccharide (p. 98).

Certain α-acetobromo-hexoses and -pentoses, notably those of D-lyxose, L-rhamnose, D-altrose, D-mannose, and D-talose give derivatives of orthoacetic acid, $CH_3C(OH)_3$, when treated with an alcohol and silver carbonate. This is the only product isolated in some cases, but in others the β-glycoside tetra-acetate is also obtained. The acetobromoaldoses that give orthoesters have the acetoxy group on $C_{(2)}$ in the axial position so that it and the $C_{(1)}$ bromine atom are in a *trans* (*ax–ax*) relationship. The $C_{(2)}$ acetyl group can therefore attack the back of $C_{(1)}$ as shown.

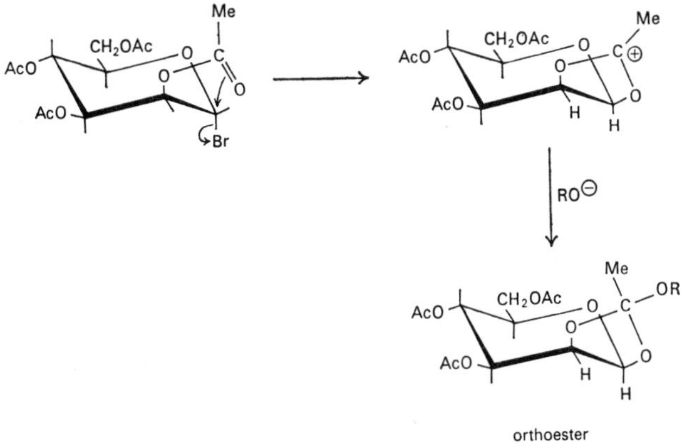

orthoester

The orthoacetates are isomeric with the corresponding glycoside tetra-acetates; the differences in reaction are, however, striking. Alkaline hydrolysis removes three of the four acetate groups from D-mannose 1,2-orthoacetate-3,4,6-triacetate to give the 1,2-orthoester. Complete deacetylation is achieved with boiling, dilute sulphuric acid. Treatment with cold methanolic hydrogen chloride leads to the rapid production of the normal methyl glycoside tetra-acetate. Extremely dilute aqueous acid removes the methyl group of the 1,2-orthoacetate with great rapidity to give the 2-O-acetyl derivative of the sugar. The rate of this reaction is about 10^{11} times that of the hydrolysis of methyl α-D-glucoside.

The positions occupied by the orthoacetate group and the presence of the pyranose ring are readily proved by the usual methylation methods. The main evidence for the orthoacetate structure is given by study of ultraviolet spectra (Braun 1930). Ordinary acetates have a characteristic band due to the unsaturated carbonyl group. This band is absent in the case of L-rhamnose methyl 1,2-orthoacetate, whose absorption between 190 and 210 mμ is practically identical with that of the structurally similar 1,2-O-isopropylidene-D-glucose.

1,2-orthoacetate group   1,2-O-isopropylidene group

Reaction of sugar 1,2-orthoesters with an alcohol, in the presence of a catalyst such as mercuric bromide, leads stereospecifically to 1,2-trans-glycosides (Kochetkov 1964).

An important phenomenon that can occur during the preparation and reactions of partially acetylated sugars is acetyl migration. Whereas methyl groups have been found to be very stable, acetyl groups sometimes change their positions under the influence of dilute alkali, often of extremely low concentration. For example, methylation of methyl β-D-glucose 2,3,4-triacetate with methyl iodide and silver oxide gives methyl 4-O-methyl-β-D-glucoside 2,3,6-triacetate. The silver oxide is sufficiently alkaline to cause an acetyl group to migrate from $C_{(4)}$ to $C_{(6)}$. This reaction involves the intermediate formation of an orthoester which, in this example, has the strainless

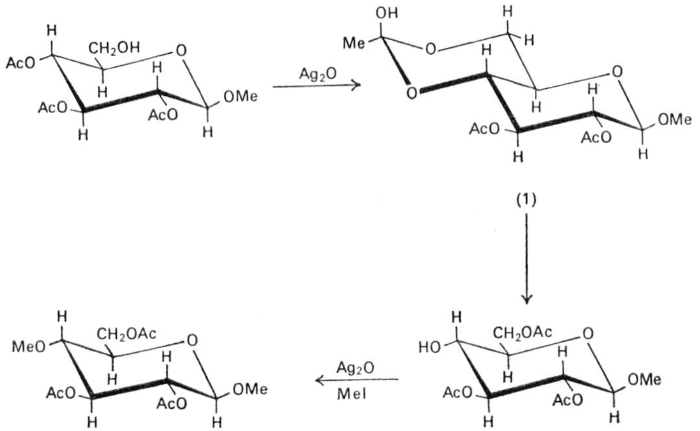

structure (1) and is therefore easily produced. Acetyl migrations
depend on the easy formation of such a cyclic intermediate.

Benzoates

Esters of benzoic acid are best prepared by treating the sugar
derivative with benzoyl chloride in pyridine, which removes the
hydrogen chloride as the pyridinium salt. By this method the

$$-\overset{|}{\underset{|}{C}}-OH + C_6H_5COCl \longrightarrow -\overset{|}{\underset{|}{C}}-O \cdot CO \cdot C_6H_5 + HCl$$

3-benzoate is obtained from $1,2 : 5,6$-di-O-isopropylidene-D-
glucose.

Benzoyl migration can occur in the presence of dilute alkali,
through an orthobenzoate intermediate; in this way $1,2$-O-iso-
propylidene-D-glucose 3-benzoate is converted into the 6-ben-
zoate.

Sulphonates

The commonest sulphonic esters of sugars are toluene-p-sul-
phonates and methanesulphonates. They are prepared by the
action of the sulphonyl chloride in pyridine on the carbohydrate
derivative. Because hydroxyl groups in different positions react
at different rates it is possible to prepare, in practical yield,
methyl a-D-glucoside 6-toluene-p-sulphonate, and methyl 4,6-
O-benzylidene-a-D-glucoside 2-toluene-p-sulphonate, as well as
the fully substituted derivatives. (The abbreviation 'mesyl' (Ms)
is used for methanesulphonyl, and 'tosyl' (Ts) for toluene-p-
sulphonyl.

When the methods for deacetylation were applied to toluene-
p-sulphonates, anomalous results were obtained (Ohle 1929,
Robertson 1933). It is now established that if a sulphonyl
group attached to a secondary carbon atom is *trans* with respect
to a neighbouring (vicinal) hydroxyl group, or ester group that
is removed under the reaction conditions, mild alkaline hydrolysis with aqueous sodium hydroxide or sodium in methanol
leads to the production of an anhydro compound with an ethyl-
ene oxide (epoxide) ring in its molecule. Furthermore, the hydrogen atom attached to the carbon atom that carried the tosyl
group is now inverted, that is, this carbon atom has undergone
a Walden inversion.

The following examples illustrate these principles.

methyl 4,6 - *O* - benzylidene - α - D -
glucoside 2 - toluene - *p* - sulphonate

methyl 2,3 - anhydro - 4, 6 - *O*-
benzylidene - α - D - mannoside

methyl α - D - glucoside
4 - toluene - *p* - sulphonate

methyl 3,4 - anhydro - α - D ⁻
galactoside

If, however, the tosyl group is isolated (i.e. there is no vicinal
hydroxyl or ester group) or if it is adjacent but *cis* to a free
hydroxyl or ester group, then hydrolysis is exceedingly difficult
to accomplish, and if it does occur is not accompanied by
epoxide formation or Walden inversion.

The explanation of this peculiar behaviour of the sulphonates

methyl α - D - galactoside
4 - toluene -*p* - sulphonate

methyl α - D - galactoside

on hydrolysis has been found by the use of water containing the oxygen isotope, ^{18}O. It was established that with a carboxylic ester the acid product of hydrolysis contained the ^{18}O, while the alcohol part did not (Polanyi 1934).

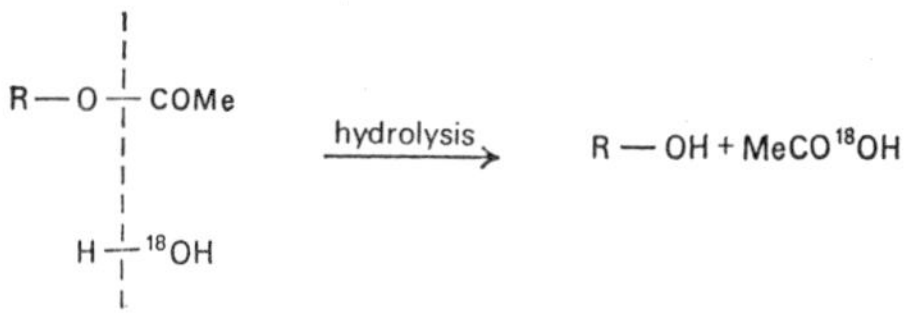

$$R-O-COMe \xrightarrow{\text{hydrolysis}} R-OH + MeCO^{18}OH$$

$$H-^{18}OH$$

With sulphonates, however, the converse was true: the alcohol contained the ^{18}O, not the acid.

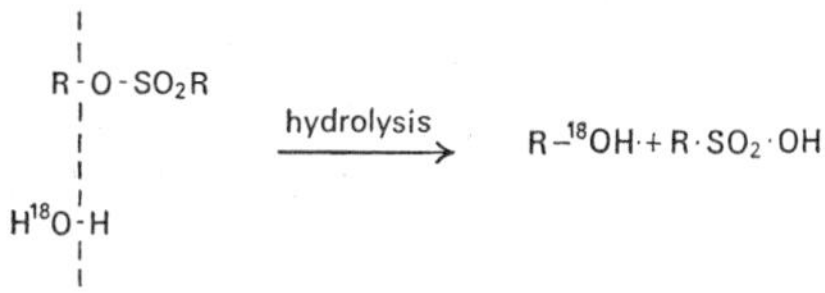

$$R-O-SO_2R \xrightarrow{\text{hydrolysis}} R-^{18}OH + R\cdot SO_2\cdot OH$$

$$H^{18}O-H$$

If a vicinal hydroxyl group is *trans* to the departing sulphonyl group then intramolecular nucleophilic attack occurs.

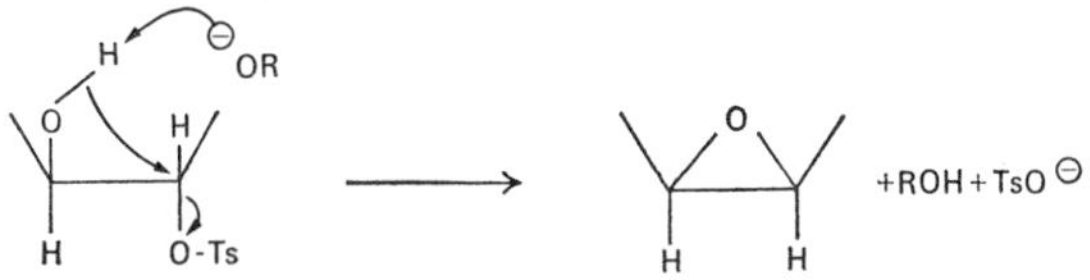

$$+ROH + TsO^{\ominus}$$

For this reaction to proceed it is necessary for the hydroxyl and tosyl groups to be in one plane. On a six-membered pyranose ring, this means both must be axial. Although methyl 4,6-*O*-benzylidene-α-D-glucoside 2-toluene-*p*-sulphonate yields the anhydro mannoside as portrayed above it has the groups involved in the reaction in equatorial positions in its most stable conformation (2). The reaction must therefore pass through the

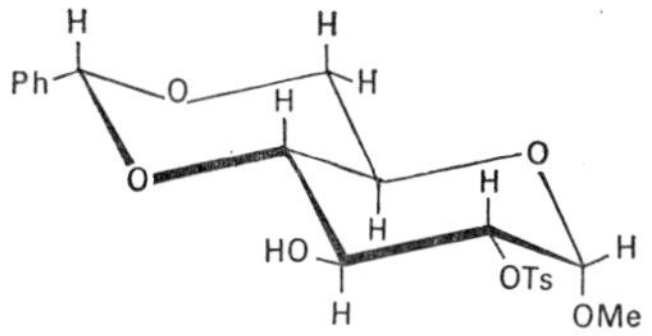

(2) 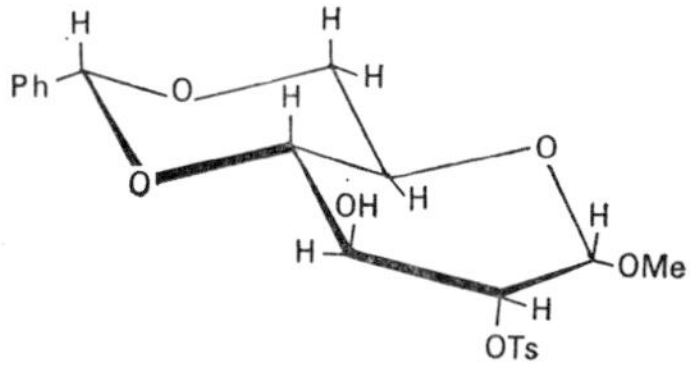   (3)

intermediate boat conformation (3) to fulfil the necessary steric requirements. This is a good example of a molecule reacting in an unfavoured conformation.

Similar boat intermediates are involved in the formation of other epoxides. Methyl 4,6-O-benzylidene-α-D-altroside 2-toluene-p-sulphonate, which has the reacting groups axial in the preferred conformer, forms an epoxide extremely rapidly in the presence of a trace of alkali (Honeyman 1958).

When a tosyl group is attached to a primary carbon atom of a sugar, an epoxide ring is formed if there is an adjacent free, or potentially free, hydroxyl group. Since the primary hydroxyl group is not asymmetric, no Walden inversion occurs. In aldohexofuranose derivatives this leads to 5,6-anhydro compounds. If, and only if, $C_{(5)}$ is substituted by a group that is less readily removed than the tosyl on $C_{(6)}$ and if there is a free hydroxyl group on $C_{(3)}$, then a 3,6-anhydro ring is produced.

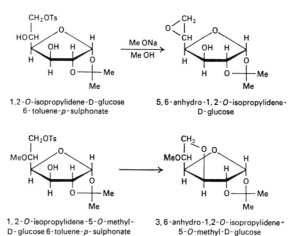

1,2-O-isopropylidene-D-glucose
6-toluene-p-sulphonate

5,6-anhydro-1,2-O-isopropylidene-
D-glucose

1,2-O-isopropylidene-5-O-methyl-
D-glucose 6-toluene-p-sulphonate

3,6-anhydro-1,2-O-isopropylidene-
5-O-methyl-D-glucose

Sulphonyl esters readily undergo nucleophilic substitution when attached to primary carbon atoms. Replacement by iodine is achieved by heating the substance with sodium iodide in acetone at 100° for 2 hours (Oldham 1922). The deoxy-iodo sugar may also undergo substitution reactions, including that with silver nitrate to give a nitrate ester.

$$\overset{|}{C}H_2OTs \xrightarrow{\text{NaI}} NaOTs + \overset{|}{C}H_2I \xrightarrow{\text{AgNO}_3} \overset{|}{C}H_2ONO_2 + AgI$$

This reaction affords a method of estimating quantitatively the amount of free primary hydroxyl in a compound containing primary and secondary hydroxyl groups. A tosyl group on $C_{(1)}$ of ketoses is, however, very difficult to replace.

Sulphonyl esters of secondary hydroxyl groups undergo nucleophilic displacement much less readily than do those of primary hydroxyl groups. The use of aprotic solvents, such as N,N-dimethylformamide (DMF), greatly facilitates these displacements that occur with inversion (S_N2 reactions); both axial and equatorial esters can be displaced. This type of reaction has become important in recent years as a method of introducing into carbohydrate derivatives a variety of groups such as F, SCN, N_3 (for reduction to NH_2) and OCOPh (for hydrolysis to the epimer of the starting sulphonate) (Baker 1959). Displacement of secondary sulphonates can also occur in other solvents, for example by use of methanolic ammonia under pressure (Lemieux 1958). Examples of such displacements are illustrated below.

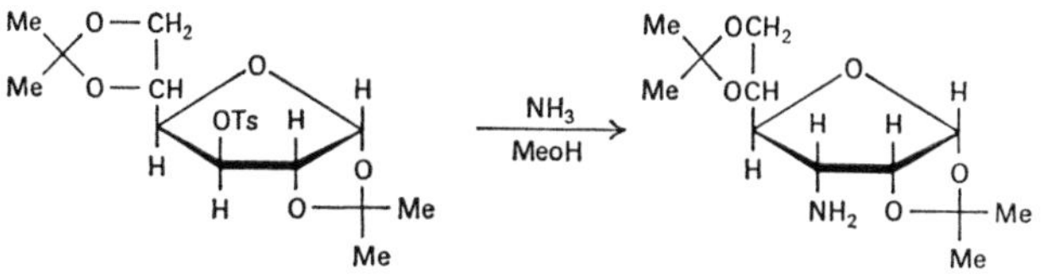

1,2:5,6-di-O-isopropylidene-D-glucose 3-toluene-p-sulphonate

3-amino-3-deoxy-1,2:5,6-di-O-isopropylidene-D-allose

methyl 4,6-di-O-tosyl-α-D-galactoside 2,3-dibenzoate

methyl α-D-glucoside 2,3,4,6-tetrabenzoate

Sulphonyl esters of primary alcohol groups are reduced with lithium aluminium hydride in ether to the corresponding deoxy ($-CH_3$) derivative. Similar treatment of the ester of a secondary alcohol gives the parent alcohol with no inversion. This is one of the better ways of removing secondary sulphonyl ester blocking groups. The two reactions are illustrated below.

methyl 2,3-di-O-methyl-β-
D-galactoside 4,6-ditoluene-
p-sulphonate

LiAlH$_4$

methyl 6-deoxy-2,3-di-O-
methyl-β-D-galactoside

Nitrates

Sugar nitrates are best prepared by treatment of a chloroform solution of the sugar derivative with a mixture of acetic anhydride and fuming nitric acid (Honeyman 1953). Another method is to use nitrogen pentoxide in chloroform (Oldham 1925).

$$\text{H}-\overset{|}{\underset{|}{\text{C}}}-\text{OH} \quad \xrightarrow[\text{CHCl}_3]{\text{Ac}_2\text{O·HNO}_3} \quad \text{H}-\overset{|}{\underset{|}{\text{C}}}-\text{ONO}_2$$

Fully nitrated carbohydrates such as those of glycerol and cellulose (erroneously called nitroglycerol and nitrocellulose) are used as explosives. Partially nitrated sugars are, however, safe to handle with care, and they are useful derivatives because of their ease of crystallization and the non-migratory nature of the nitrate groups.

Nitrate groups can react either like carboxylic or sulphonyl esters. Denitration without Walden inversion or anhydro formation is effected by reductive methods, such as the reaction with hydrazine or catalytic hydrogenation. The latter method, in which the yields are almost quantitative, cannot be used if the sugar derivative contains other reducible groups (L. P. Kuhn 1946).

The removal by alkaline hydrolysis of nitrate groups attached to C$_{(6)}$ gives the same product as from the corresponding sulphonyl ester (Purves 1944). Thus methyl α-D-glucoside 2,3,4-triacetate 6-nitrate with aqueous or alcoholic sodium hydroxide gives methyl 3,6-anhydro-α-D-glucoside.

The nitrate group on a primary carbon atom undergoes nucleophilic replacement in the same way as sulphonates, notably when heated with sodium iodide in acetone.

$$\overset{|}{\text{CH}_2\text{ONO}_2} \quad \rightarrow \quad \overset{|}{\text{CH}_2\text{I}} + \text{NO}_3-$$

However, a secondary nitrate is converted by sodium iodide in acetone into the corresponding hydroxyl compound. Sodium nitrite in boiling aqueous ethanol removes secondary nitrates to yield the corresponding alcohol; primary nitrates react slowly, if at all.

Sulphates

Sulphates of sugar derivatives may be prepared by use of chlorosulphonic acid, $ClSO_2OH$, or sulphur trioxide in pyridine.

$$H-\overset{|}{\underset{|}{C}}-OH \xrightarrow[\text{pyridine}]{Cl \cdot SO_2OH} H-\overset{|}{\underset{|}{C}}-OSO_2OH$$

Sulphate esters occur naturally in many seaweed polysaccharides. Heparin, the naturally occurring blood anticoagulating agent, is a sulphated polysaccharide, which also contains N-sulphate groups, $-NHSO_2OH$. The reactions of the sulphate group are similar to those of the sulphonates.

Phosphates

Sugar phosphates are very important biochemically. They occur as components of nucleic acids and are intermediates in many metabolic processes, such as photosynthesis and fermentation.

Aldose 1-phosphates are readily prepared by the reaction of an acetobromoaldose with silver phosphate; α-D-glucopyranose 1-phosphate may be made in this way (Cori 1937).

The most general method for preparing other phosphate esters is by using a disubstituted phosphoryl monochloride $ClP(O)(OR)_2$, for example diphenyl, dibenzyl, or catechol

$$-\overset{|}{\underset{|}{C}}OH + ClP\overset{O}{\underset{OCH_2Ph}{\overset{\|}{\diagup}}}_{OCH_2Ph} \xrightarrow{\text{pyridine}} -\overset{|}{\underset{|}{C}}OP\overset{O}{\underset{OCH_2Ph}{\overset{\|}{\diagup}}}_{OCH_2Ph} \xrightarrow{[H]} -\overset{|}{\underset{|}{C}}OP(OH)_2$$

sugar phosphate

$$sugar \overset{|}{\underset{|}{-C}}OH + ClP\overset{O}{\diagup} \xrightarrow{\text{pyridine}} -\overset{|}{\underset{|}{C}}OP\overset{O}{\diagup} \xrightarrow{H_2O} -\overset{|}{\underset{|}{C}}OP(OH)_2 +$$

phosphochloridate. The reaction is carried out in pyridine and the protecting aromatic groups are removed by hydrolysis with dilute acid, or hydrogenolysis, or in the case of the catechol derivative, treatment with water.

The use of heavy oxygen water has shown that the hydrolysis of phosphates follows a course similar to that of carboxylic (and not sulphonic) esters.

Phosphate esters can migrate in the presence of dilute acid (Levene 1934).

ANHYDRO SUGARS

Anhydro sugars can be considered to result from the elimination of water from a pair of hydroxyl groups in a sugar.

1,6-Anhydro-aldoses

These have already been mentioned on p. 40. They may also be prepared by the pyrolysis of polysaccharides. In this way cellulose gives 1,6-anhydro-β-D-glucopyranose (lævoglucosan) and ivory nut mannan gives 1,6-anhydro-β-D-mannopyranose (lævomannosan).

Treatment of acetohalogeno sugars with trimethylamine followed by barium hydroxide gives 1,6-anhydro-sugars (Karrer 1921).

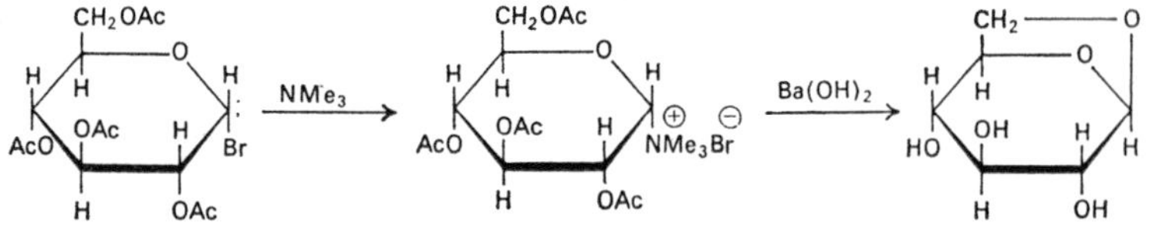

acetobromoglucose　　　　　　　　　　　　　　　　　　laevoglucosan

The structure of 1,6-anhydro-β-D-glucopyranose has been proved because methylation followed by hydrolysis gives 2,3,4-tri-O-methyl-D-glucose.

As mentioned earlier (p. 40) the 1,6-anhydro-hexopyranoses must exist in the CE (D-1C, L-C1) conformation.

3,6-Anhydro-aldoses

These are prepared from sulphonates or nitrates as described earlier in this chapter (p. 60).

3,6-Anhydro-pyranosides exist in a strained conformation as shown:

3,6 -anhydrohexopyranoses

This strain is relieved whenever possible by molecular rearrangement to the furanoside forms.

Epoxides

The preparation of sugar epoxides from sulphonate esters has been described earlier in this chapter (p. 59). They may also be prepared by de-amination with nitrous acid of suitably blocked *trans* diaxial a-hydroxyamino compounds.

Epoxide rings may be opened by the attack of nucleophilic reagents, e.g. $OH^{\ominus}$, $OMe^{\ominus}$, $NH_2^{\ominus}$, $N_3^{\ominus}$, or $PhS^{\ominus}$ or acidic reagents, e.g. $Cl^{\ominus}$ or $Br^{\ominus}$, to give products with the *trans* configurations.

Rigidly held pyranose epoxides open to give mainly the products with *trans* (*ax–ax*) substituents with minor amounts of the *trans* (*eq–eq*) products (Furst–Plattner Rule; Mills 1953).

For example,

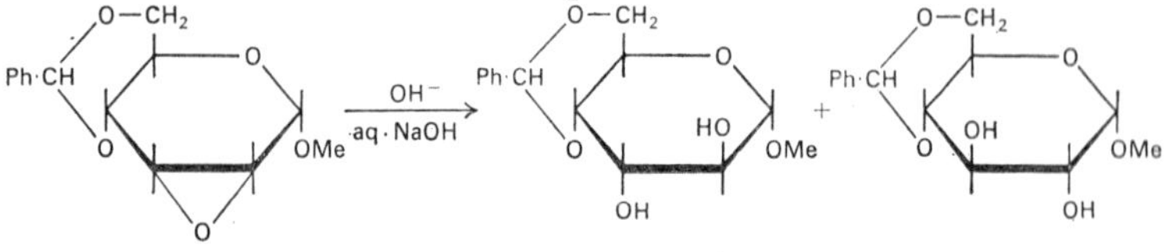

| methyl 2, 3 - anhydro -
4,6 -O - benzylidene-
α-D- alloside | methyl 4, 6 - O -
benzylidene - α -
D - altroside
(84 per cent) | methyl 4, 6 - O -
benzylidene -
α - D - glucoside
(7 per cent) |

(For other examples, see pp. 76, 86.) These reactions enable a rare sugar to be made from a common one, e.g. methyl α-D-glucoside may be converted into methyl α-D-altroside:

methyl α-D-glucopyranoside
↓
methyl 4, 6 - O - benzylidene - α-D-glucoside
↓
methyl 4, 6 - O - benzylidene - α - D - glucoside 2, 3 - ditosylate
↓
methyl 2,3-anhydro - 4,6-O-benzylidene - α - D-alloside
↓
methyl 4,6-O- benzylidene-α-D-altroside
↓
methyl α-D-altropyranoside

The conformation of a pyranose ring bearing an epoxide ring is the 'half-chair', with four adjacent pyranose ring atoms in one plane as shown below for a pyranose 2,3-epoxide.

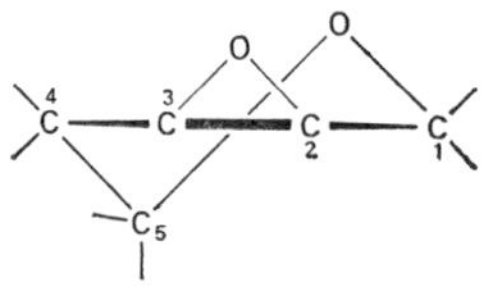

The substituents at $C_{(5)}$ remain truly axial and equatorial, but those at $C_{(1)}$ and $C_{(4)}$ become approximately equally inclined to the plane of the four adjacent ring atoms (so-called 'quasi-equatorial' and 'quasi-axial' bonds).

REVIEWS

Carbonates and thiocarbonates of carbohydrates, by L. Hough, J. E. Priddle, and R. S. Theobald, *Adv. Carbohyd. Chem.* 1960, **15**, 91.

Carbohydrate *ortho*esters, by E. Pacsu, *Adv. Carbohyd. Chem.* 1945, **1**, 77.

Glycosyl halides and their derivatives, by L. J. Haynes and F. H. Newth, *Adv. Carbohyd. Chem.* 1955, **10**, 207.

Glycals, by B. Helferich, *Adv. Carbohyd. Chem.* 1952, **7**, 209.

Sulphonic esters of carbohydrates, by R. S. Tipson, *Adv. Carbohyd. Chem.* 1953, **8**, 107.

Sugar nitrates, by J. Honeyman and J. W. W. Morgan, *Adv. Carbohyd. Chem.* 1957, **12**, 117.

Sugar phosphates, by A. B. Foster and W. G. Overend, *Q. Rev. chem. Soc.* 1957, **11**, 61.

Sugar epoxides, by F. H. Newth, *Q. Rev. chem. Soc.* 1959, **13**, 30.

Sulphates of the simple sugars, by J. R. Turvey, *Adv. Carbohyd. Chem.* 1965, **20**, 183.

Neighbouring group participation in sugars, by L. Goodman, *Adv. Carbohyd. Chem.*, 1967, **22**, 109.

9

GLYCOL-SPLITTING REAGENTS

Metaperiodic acid and its sodium and potassium salts

THE cleavage of α-glycol groups by sodium or potassium metaperiodate in aqueous solutions was discovered by Malaprade (1928), and its specificity was shown by Fleury and Lange (1932). The carbon chain is broken and two aldehyde groups are produced.

$$\begin{array}{c} | \\ \mathrm{CHOH} \\ | \\ \mathrm{CHOH} \\ | \end{array} + \mathrm{IO_4^-} \longrightarrow \begin{array}{c} | \\ \mathrm{CHO} \\ \\ \mathrm{CHO} \\ | \end{array} + \mathrm{IO_3^-} + \mathrm{H_2O}$$

Other groups that are also oxidized include α-amino alcohols, α-hydroxyaldehydes, and α-hydroxyketones.

Compounds containing three hydroxyl groups on adjacent carbon atoms are oxidized by two molecular proportions of periodate and are cleaved to yield two aldehyde groups and one molecular proportion of formic acid. Four adjacent hydroxyl groups lead to two molecular proportions of formic acid and so on. The amount of acid may be determined by titration to give information about the arrangement of hydroxyl groups in a polyhydroxy molecule.

$$\begin{array}{c} | \\ \mathrm{CHOH} \\ | \\ \mathrm{CHOH} \\ | \\ \mathrm{CHOH} \\ | \end{array} \xrightarrow{\mathrm{IO_4^\ominus}} \begin{array}{c} | \\ \mathrm{CHO} \\ \\ \mathrm{CHO} \\ | \\ \mathrm{CHOH} \\ | \end{array} \xrightarrow{\mathrm{IO_4^\ominus}} \begin{array}{c} | \\ \mathrm{CHO} \\ \\ \mathrm{HCO_2H} \\ \\ \mathrm{CHO} \\ | \end{array}$$

If a primary alcohol group is involved in the oxidation then formaldehyde is produced. The amount of this may be measured and used to determine the number of primary hydroxyl groups in a polyhydroxy molecule.

$$-\mathrm{CHOH-CH_2OH} \longrightarrow -\mathrm{CHO} + \mathrm{CH_2O}$$

The oxidation is usually carried out in aqueous solution using periodic acid for solutions of pH < 4, sodium metaperiodate for solutions of pH 4–7, and the potassium salt for alkaline oxidations. Most oxidations are carried out at pH about 4, in the dark to avoid over-oxidation and decomposition of the oxidant (Head 1950). Periodate consumption is measured by releasing iodine from the periodate ion and determining it by titration.

The oxidation is believed to occur by formation of a cyclic ester, which then decomposes to the products (Criegee 1933, Bunton 1954). For cyclic compounds *cis* α-glycols react more rapidly than *trans* ones; this is because of ease of formation of

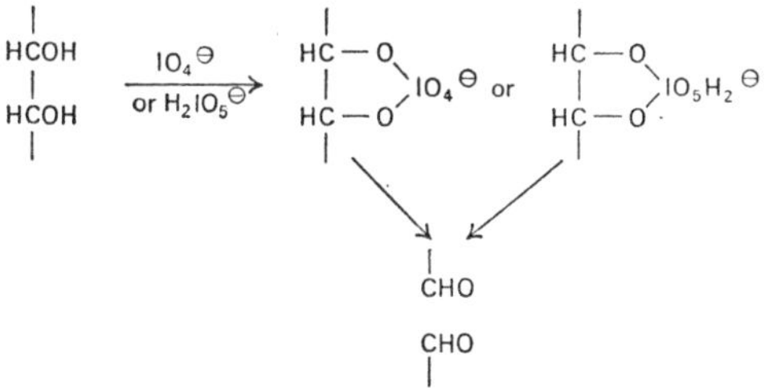

the bicyclic complex. However, α-glycol groups in which the hydroxyl groups are rigidly held at 180° apart (i.e. diaxial arrangement) are not oxidized because the intermediate cyclic ester is sterically impossible to form. Examples are methyl 4,6-O-benzylidene-α-D-altroside (1) (Honeyman 1959) and 1,6-anhydro-β-D-glucofuranose (2).

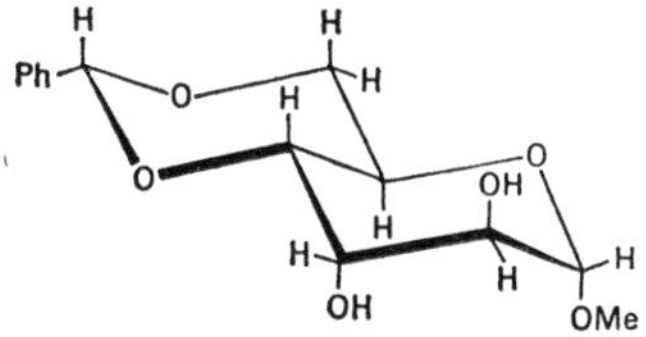

(1) 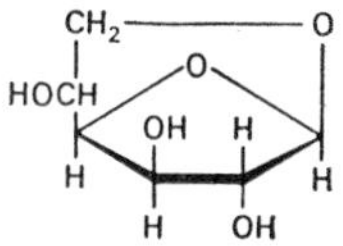   (2)

Uses of the reaction

Periodate oxidation has been successfully used to determine the number, type, and arrangement of adjacent hydroxyl groups in a molecule; to determine polysaccharide structures (see pp. 109, 111, 113); and to determine the size of the ring in glycosides (Hudson 1936). Normal glycosides were shown to be pyranosides because they reduced two moles of periodate, and gave one mole of formic acid and no formaldehyde. The dialdehydes were not isolated, but were oxidized with bromine water in the

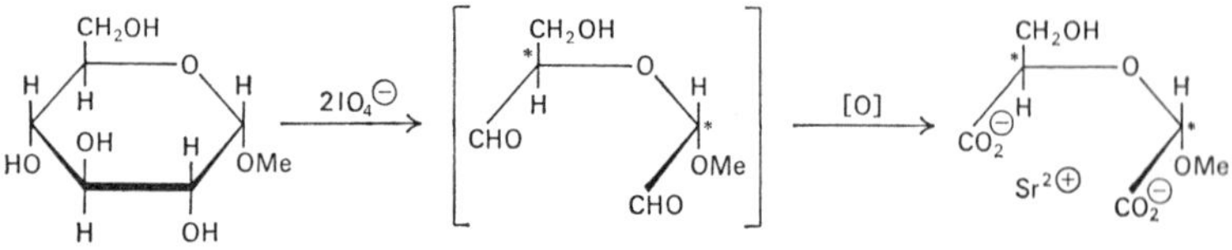

methyl α-D-glucopyranoside

presence of strontium hydroxide. The constitution of the resulting strontium salt was proved by its hydrolysis to oxalic and D-glyceric acids. In the dialdehyde and the acid there are only two asymmetric carbon atoms (*) corresponding to $C_{(1)}$ and $C_{(5)}$ of the glycoside. It has been found that all methyl α-D-aldohexopyranosides give the same oxidation product and so all must have the same configuration on $C_{(1)}$. Similarly for all the β-D-aldohexopyranosides.

Oxidation of methyl aldopentopyranosides follows a similar course.

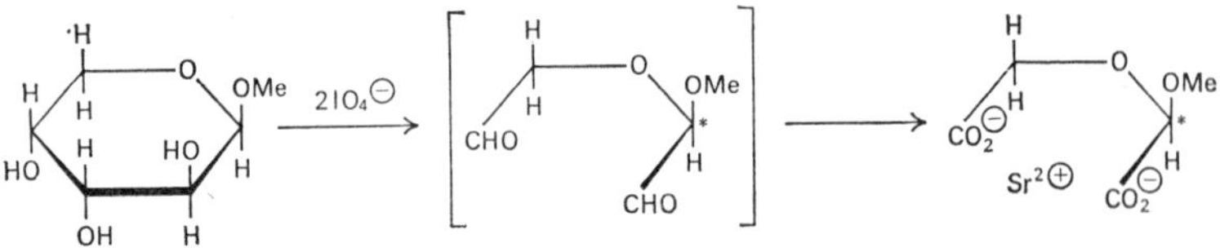

methyl β-D-
arabinopyranoside

Here there is only one asymmetric carbon atom in the product. All methyl α-D-aldopentopyranosides yield the same products and the β-compounds give the enantiomorph.

Although methyl α-D-arabinofuranoside requires only one mole of periodate for oxidation it yields the same oxidation product as methyl α-D-glucopyranoside.

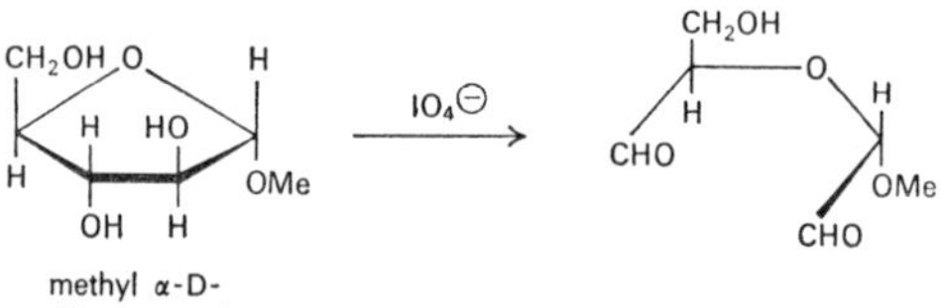

methyl α-D-
arabinofuranoside

In a modification of Hudson's approach the dialdehydes from the oxidation of methyl aldohexopyranosides are reduced with aqueous sodium borohydride (Smith 1955). The reduced products contain only one asymmetric carbon atom, the original

$C_{(1)}$. Again structural correlations can be made between different glycosides.

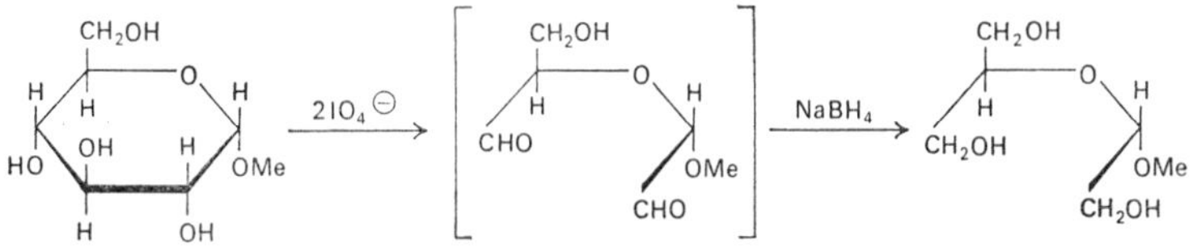

methyl α-D-glucopyranoside

This method has been largely superseded by structural assignments based on nuclear magnetic resonance spectra (see p. 134).

The uptake of periodate cannot be used to determine the ring size in amino-sugar glycosides, as it has been shown that some furanosides of amino-sugars react anomalously (Weiss 1959).

Pyranoside derivatives of amino-sugars are oxidized normally, with the exception (cf. diols) of rigidly held diaxial systems, which oxidized extremely slowly (Guthrie 1966).

Structure and reactions of the products

The product from the oxidation of methyl 4,6-O-benzylidene-α-D-glucoside has been shown to be the hemialdal (3); this is in equilibrium in water with the dialdehyde form since derivatives of both have been prepared (Honeyman 1958). Because (3) contains —O—CHOH— groups it resembles a free sugar in many of its reactions including those with aromatic amines, and with methyl iodide and silver oxide.

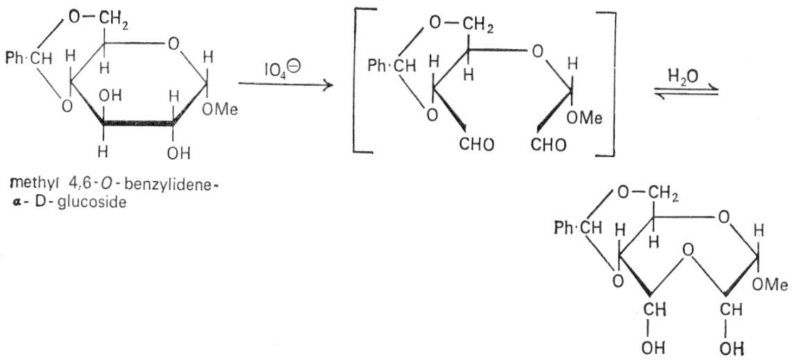

methyl 4,6-O-benzylidene-α-D-glucoside

(3)

The product from methyl α-D-glucoside also does not behave as a simple dialdehyde; derivatives of the forms below have been isolated (Smith 1957–60).

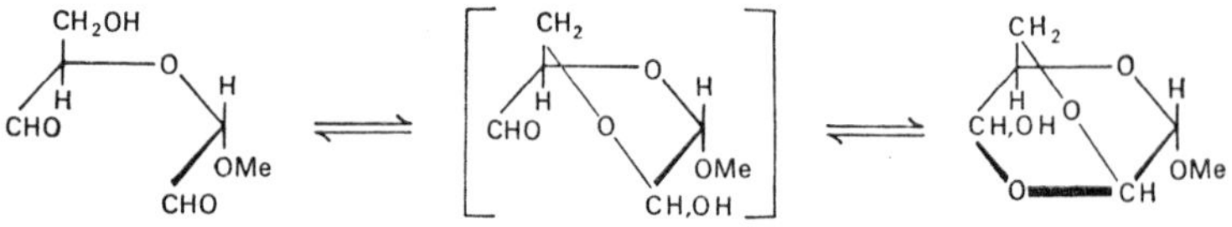

The results from chemical studies are supported by study of the proton magnetic resonance spectra of the oxidation products (Perlin 1966).

The products from periodate oxidation have recently found use in amino-sugar synthesis (see pp. 76, 77).

Lead tetra-acetate

Oxidations with lead tetra-acetate are similar to those by periodate, but the solvents used, usually glacial acetic acid, are not so generally suitable. The oxidation is also believed to occur via a cyclic ester intermediate, similar to that postulated for oxidation by periodate (Criegee 1933).

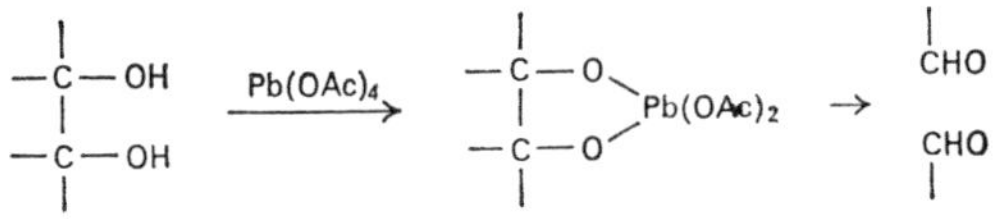

Lead tetra-acetate in pyridine has been found to oxidize rigidly held diaxial diols, such as methyl 4,6-O-benzylidene-α-D-altroside (Perlin 1960).

REVIEWS
Periodate oxidation of carbohydrates, by J. M. Bobbitt, *Adv. Carbohyd. Chem.* 1956, **11**, 1.

The action of lead tetra-acetate on the sugars, by A. S. Perlin, *Adv. Carbohyd. Chem.* 1959, **14**, 9.

The 'dialdehydes' from the periodate oxidation of carbohydrates, by R. D. Guthrie, *Adv. Carbohyd. Chem.* 1961, **16**, 105.

Organic chemistry of periodates, by B. Sklarz, *Q. Rev. chem. Soc.* 1967, **21**, 3.

Glycol cleavage and related reactions, by C. A. Bunton, in *Oxidation in organic chemistry* (ed. K. B. Wiberg), p. 367 (Academic Press, New York, 1965).

10

NITROGEN-CONTAINING MONOSACCHARIDE DERIVATIVES

Glycosylamines

GLYCOSYLAMINES contain the amino group in place of the anomeric hydroxyl group. Derivatives of primary and secondary amines are named as N-substituted glycosylamines. Compounds from heretocyclic bases are generally named as derivatives of the base, e.g. N-(D-glucosyl)-piperidine. N-Arylglycosylamines are particularly common and easy to prepare.

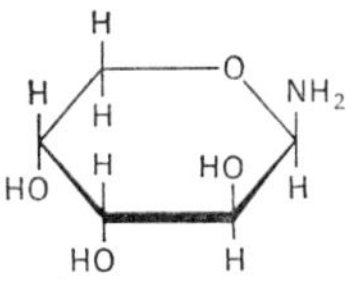

β - D - arabinosylamine

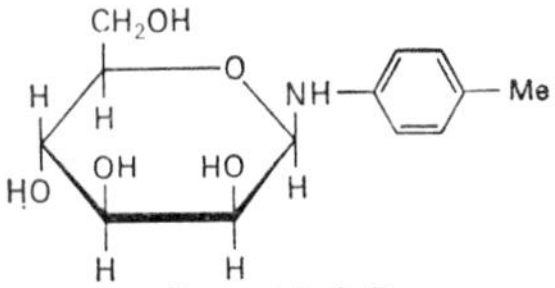

N - p - tolyl - β - D - mannosylamine

The general method of preparation is to add the sugar to the amine in aqueous alcohol containing a trace of acid.

Many glycosylamines and their N-substituted derivatives are unusual in that although $C_{(1)}$ is substituted they can mutarotate. This means that in solution cyclic and acyclic forms are present in equilibrium.

Acetylation and benzoylation proceed under mild conditions; hydrolysis of the products with dilute acid gives esters (such as D-glucose 2,3,4,6-tetra-acetate) unsubstituted on $C_{(1)}$ which show that the original sugar derivative has reacted in the pyranose form. Methylation, followed by hydrolysis, leads to the methyl ether of the pyranose form unsubstituted on $C_{(1)}$ (such as 2,3,4,6-tetra-O-methyl-D-glucose).

Glycosylamines rearrange in the presence of acid to 1-amino-1-deoxy-ketoses (Amadori 1925). This product may be obtained directly from sugar and an amine by using sufficient acid catalyst.

$$\begin{array}{c}
\text{CHNHPh} \\
| \\
\text{HCOH} \\
| \\
\text{HOCH} \\
| \\
\text{HCOH} \\
| \\
\text{HC} \longrightarrow \text{O} \\
| \\
\text{CH}_2\text{OH}
\end{array}
\quad \longrightarrow \quad
\begin{array}{c}
\text{CH}_2\text{NHPh} \\
| \\
\text{C} \longrightarrow \text{OH} \\
| \\
\text{HOCH} \\
| \\
\text{HCOH} \\
| \\
\text{HCOH} \\
| \\
\text{CH}_2 \longrightarrow \text{O}
\end{array}$$

N - phenyl - D - glucosylamine   1 - anilino - 1 - deoxy -
                                    D - fructose

The mechanism (Weygand 1939) of the rearrangement is:

$$\begin{array}{c}
\text{CH} \longrightarrow \text{NH} \longrightarrow \text{R} \\
| \quad \diagdown \\
\text{H} \longrightarrow \text{C} \longrightarrow \text{OH} \\
|
\end{array}
\rightleftharpoons
\begin{array}{c}
\text{CH} = \text{N} \longrightarrow \text{R} \\
| \\
\text{H} \longrightarrow \text{C} \longrightarrow \text{OH} \\
|
\end{array}
\quad \text{H}^{\oplus} \rightarrow$$

$$\begin{array}{c}
\text{CH} \longrightarrow \text{NH} \longrightarrow \text{R} \\
\| \\
\text{C} \longrightarrow \text{OH} \\
|
\end{array}
\rightarrow
\begin{array}{c}
\text{CH}_2\text{NHR} \\
| \\
\text{CO} \\
|
\end{array}
\rightarrow
\begin{array}{c}
\text{CH}_2\text{NHR} \\
| \\
\text{C} \longrightarrow \text{OH} \\
|
\end{array}$$

Nucleosides and nucleotides

Nucleosides are compounds of the glycosylamine type derived from a sugar and a purine or pyrimidine base. The most important members are the naturally occurring derivatives of D-ribose and 2-deoxy-D-ribose, which have the sugar in the furanose form. Two examples are illustrated.

1 - (β -D- ribofuranosyl) -uracil   9- (β -D- ribofuranosyl) - guanine
       (uridine)   (guanosine)

Nucleotides are phosphate esters of nucleosides. Nucleic acids which are important constituents of cell cytoplasm, are polymeric nucleotides; the nucleotide units are linked by phosphate ester bonds. The two most important are ribonucleic and deoxyribonucleic acids (RNA and DNA).

Amino sugars

Amino sugars may be regarded as being derived from sugars by replacement of OH by NH_2 at any carbon atom except $C_{(1)}$ in aldoses and $C_{(2)}$ in ketoses. They occur widely in nature in the polysaccharides of the shell of crustacea (crabs, lobsters) and as components of many antibiotics, including streptomycin and neomycin. Until recently most attention has been given to the 2-amino-2-deoxyaldoses.

Several methods have been used for preparing amino sugars.

1. Acid hydrolysis of the chitin of lobster shells gives good yields of 2-amino-2-deoxy-D-glucose, often called D-glucosamine or chitosamine. Similarly, 2-amino-2-deoxy-D-galactose (also known as D-galactosamine or chondrosamine) can be prepared by acid hydrolysis of chondroitin, a polysaccharide constituent of cartilage and nasal mucilage.

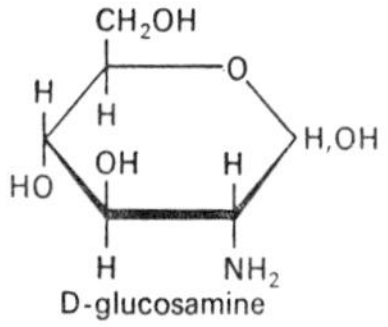

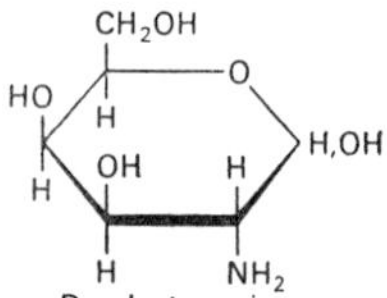

2. Addition of hydrogen cyanide to an aldose in the presence of ammonia or an amine yields a pair of epimeric a-amino nitriles, which may be separated and then hydrogenated using a platinum catalyst in the presence of acid to the amino aldoses containing one more carbon atom (E. Fischer 1903, Wolfrom 1946, R. Kuhn 1955).

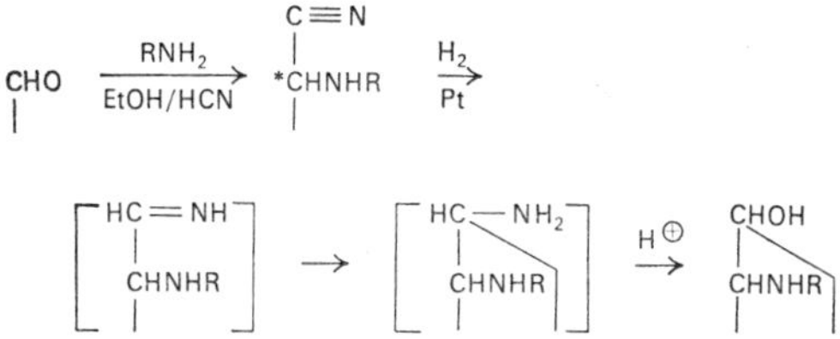

*new asymmetric centre; R = H,aryl, alkyl

When R is a benzyl or phenyl group, it may be removed by hydrogenolysis. An example of this reaction is the synthesis from L-arabinose of the rare sugars L-glucosamine and L-mannosamine. All possible 2-amino-2-deoxy-hexoses, and -pentoses have been synthesized by this route.

3. Sugar epoxides react at 100° in a sealed tube with ammonia in methanol, or with liquid ammonia, to give a mixture of the two possible *trans* amino sugars with the diaxial product predominating. The same product can be obtained by opening the epoxide ring with azide ion, followed by reduction.

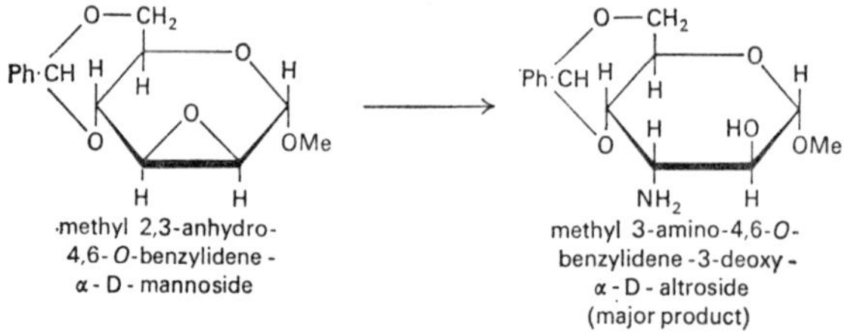
O—CH2
Ph·CH
O
OMe
NH2
HO
methyl 2,3-anhydro-4,6-O-benzylidene-α-D-mannoside
methyl 3-amino-4,6-O-benzylidene-3-deoxy-α-D-altroside (major product)

4. A *trans* α-amino alcohol is converted by partial acetylation followed by treatment with methanesulphonyl chloride in pyridine into its *N*-acetyl-*O*-methanesulphonyl derivative which, with sodium or potassium acetate in aqueous 2-methoxyethanol, yields the *cis* *N*-acetylamino alcohol (Baker 1953). For example (Jeanloz 1957):

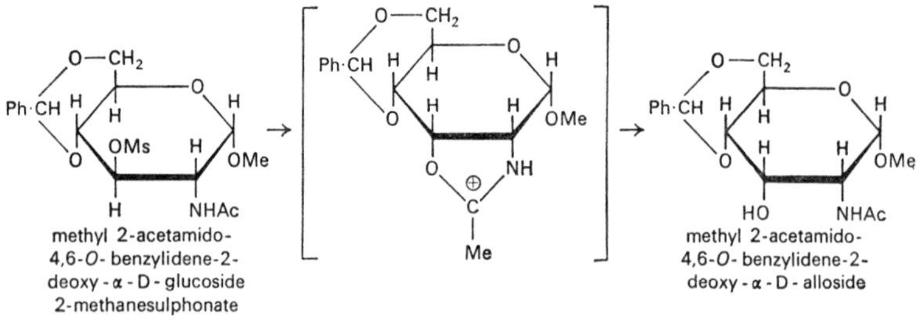
O—CH2
Ph·CH
OMs
OMe
NHAc
NH
Me
HO
methyl 2-acetamido-4,6-O-benzylidene-2-deoxy-α-D-glucoside 2-methanesulphonate
methyl 2-acetamido-4,6-O-benzylidene-2-deoxy-α-D-alloside

A component of the antibiotic puromycin, 3-amino-3-deoxy-D-ribose, has also been synthesized by this route (Baker 1954).

5. Reaction of a dialdehyde with nitromethane in the presence of sodium methoxide gives a cyclic nitro compound that is easily reduced to the corresponding amino sugar (H. O. L. Fischer 1958).

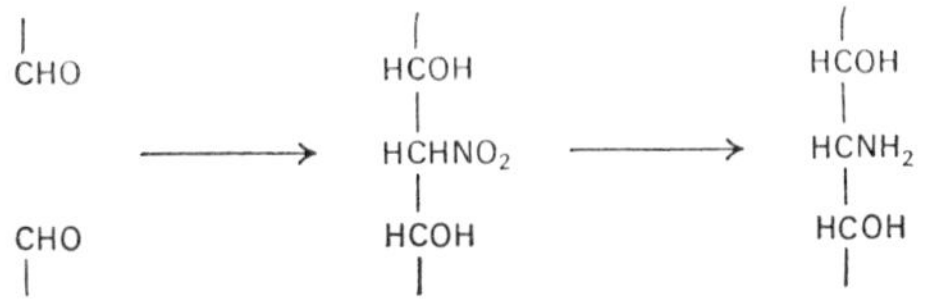

from methyl α-D-glucoside   methyl 3 amino-3-deoxy
                                                α-D-mannoside

6. Reaction of a dialdehyde with phenylhydrazine gives a phenylazo derivative that may be reduced to the corresponding amino sugar (Guthrie 1960).

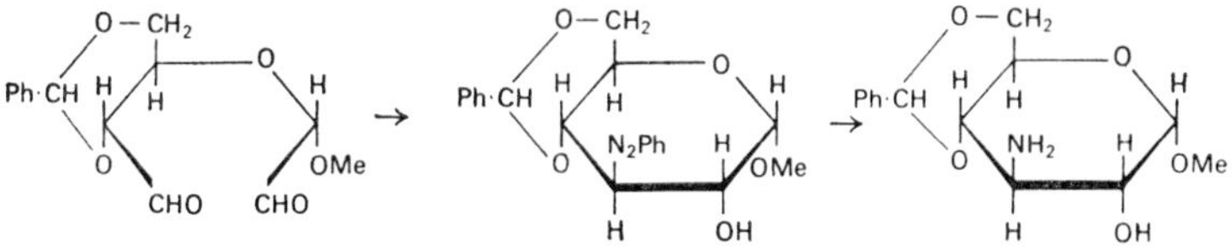

from methyl 4,6-O-   methyl 3-amino-4,6-O-
benzylidene-α-D-   benzylidene-3-deoxy-
glucoside   α-D-glucoside

The amino sugars undergo many of the reactions of sugars including mutarotation, and osazone formation, with loss of the —NH_2 group if on $C_{(2)}$.

Acetylation of amino sugars can lead to derivatives containing both O- and N-acetyl groups. N-Acetyl derivatives are prepared by preferential acetylation techniques, or by complete O- and m-acetylation followed by catalytic deacetylation with sodium

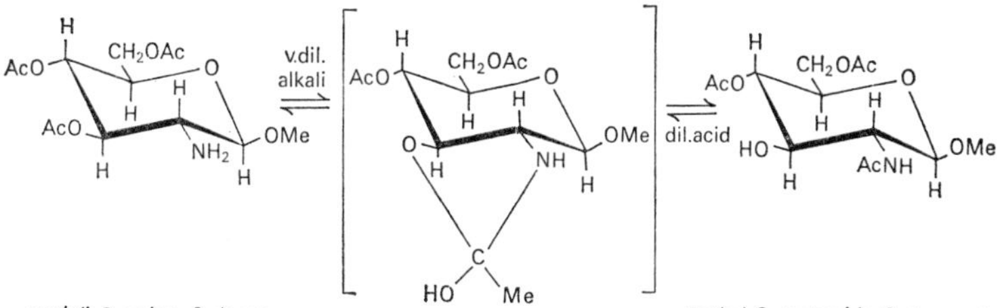

methyl 2-amino-2-deoxy-   methyl 2-acetamido-2-deoxy-β-
β-D-glucoside 2,4,6-   D-glucoside-4,6-diacetate
triacetate

in methanol to remove the O-acetyl groups. Both $O \to N$ and $N \to O$ acetyl migration can occur presumably through cyclic intermediates (cf. p. 56).

Glycosides are not obtained by treating 2-amino-2-deoxy-hexoses with acid–alcohol mixtures because of the formation of the electrostatically shielding $-\overset{\oplus}{N}H_3$ group; when the amino group is blocked, for example, by acetylation to an acetamido group, then glycosidation occurs.

Amino-sugar derivatives containing an α-amino alcohol group are generally cleaved by periodate to give the product similarly obtained from the corresponding α-glycol; some furanosides react anomalously.

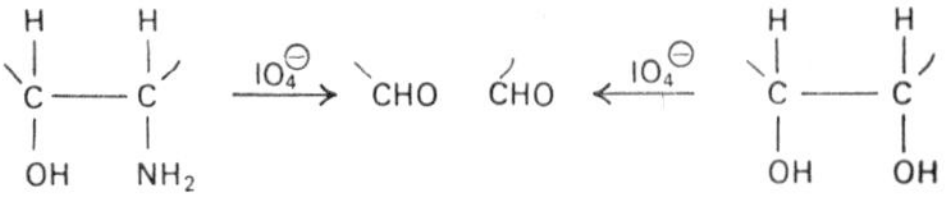

$$\overset{H}{\underset{OH}{\overset{|}{\underset{|}{C}}}} - \overset{H}{\underset{NH_2}{\overset{|}{\underset{|}{C}}}} \xrightarrow{IO_4^{\ominus}} CHO \quad \dot{C}HO \xleftarrow{IO_4^{\ominus}} \overset{H}{\underset{OH}{\overset{|}{\underset{|}{C}}}} - \overset{H}{\underset{OH}{\overset{|}{\underset{|}{C}}}}$$

Nonulosaminic acids (sialic acids)

These are amino-sugar derivatives occurring, combined, in animal tissues including those of the brain; the commonest of these is neuraminic acid.

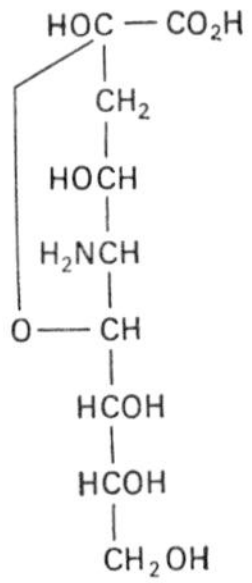

$$
\begin{array}{l}
HOC - CO_2H \\
\quad | \\
\quad CH_2 \\
\quad | \\
HOCH \\
\quad | \\
H_2NCH \\
\quad | \\
O - CH \\
\quad | \\
HCOH \\
\quad | \\
HCOH \\
\quad | \\
CH_2OH
\end{array}
$$

neuraminic acid

Phenylhydrazine derivatives

Aldoses and ketoses react with phenylhydrazine to yield phenylhydrazones, which react further to give osazones (see p. 7) (Fischer 1887).

Three molecular proportions of phenylhydrazine are needed and ammonia and aniline are formed.

The mechanism of osazone formation has been studied by

many groups of workers for eighty years and still no completely satisfactory scheme has emerged. It seems probable that different mechanisms may apply under different conditions. The reaction is difficult to study because of simultaneous side reactions.

The mechanisms that have been proposed are basically of two types involving either an oxidation step (dehydrogenation) (Fischer type of mechanism) or an Amadori rearrangement. A recent review provides excellent documentation of the work in this field (El Khadem 1965).

Although often used, osazones are not particularly good derivatives for identifying sugars because of their variable melting points. If an osazone is heated in aqueous copper sulphate an osotriazole is produced that is easily purified to give a crystalline compound with sharp and characteristic melting point (Hudson 1944).

<pre>
CH:N·NHPh   CH:N
 | -------> | N·Ph
C:N·NHPh   C:N
 |

 osazone   osotriazole
</pre>

The phenylhydrazine residues may be removed from osazones by hydrolysis or by reaction with benzaldehyde to give osones which, like sugars, exist in cyclic modifications.

<pre>
CH:N·NHPh   CHO
 | -------> |
C:N·NHPh   CO
 | |
 osazone   osone
</pre>

REVIEWS

Glycosylamines, by J. Honeyman and G. P. Ellis, *Adv. Carbohyd. Chem.* 1955, **10**, 95.

Amadori rearrangement, by J. E. Hodge, *Adv. Carbohyd. Chem.* 1955, **10**, 169.

Maillard reaction, by G. P. Ellis, *Adv. Carbohyd. Chem.* 1959, **14**, 63.

Chemistry of the amino-sugars, by A. B. Foster and D. Horton, *Adv. Carbohyd. Chem.* 1959, 14, 213.

Nucleic acids, by G. R. Barker, *Adv. Carbohyd. Chem.* 1956, **11**, 285.

Neuraminic acids and related compounds, by F. Zilliken and M. W. Whitehouse, *Adv. Carbohyd. Chem.* 1958, **13**, 237.

Chemistry of the amino-sugars derived from antibiotic substances, by J. D. Dutcher, *Adv. Carbohyd. Chem.* 1963, **18**, 259.

Chemistry of osazones, by H. El Khadem, *Adv. Carbohyd. Chem.* 1965, **20**, 139.

11

MISCELLANEOUS MONOSACCHARIDE DERIVATIVES AND POLYOLS

1. Aldulose derivatives

'Ulose' is the systematic name-ending given a sugar derivative containing a ketonic carbonyl group. Thus (1) (see below) is methyl α-D-*xylo*hexopyranosid-4-ulose.

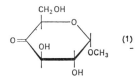

methyl α-D-*xylo*hexopyranosid-4-ulose

Derivatives of alduloses are important because of the different compounds that can be made by exploiting the synthetic possibilities of the carbonyl group: reduction may yield the epimer of the starting alcohol; a variety of addition reactions yield branched-chain sugar derivatives; reduction of the oxime gives amino-sugars.

Most of the methods used to oxidize secondary hydroxyl groups, and therefore to prepare alduloses, require the use of a derivative in which all the remaining hydroxyl groups are substituted. The best oxidation methods are those based on dimethylsulphoxide (DMSO). Pfitzner and Moffatt (1963) discovered that DMSO in conjunction with dicyclohexylcarbodiimide (DCC) $(C_6H_{11}N{=}C{=}NC_6H_{11})$ in the presence of phosphoric acid or pyridinium trifluoroacetate smoothly oxidized isolated hydroxyl groups to the corresponding aldehyde or ketone in high yield. Acid anhydrides such as acetic anhydride (Albright and Goldman 1965) or phosphoric anhydride (Onodera 1965) in DMSO have also been used successfully. These last reactions are mechanistically related to the Pfitzner–Moffatt method, also proceeding via alkoxy-sulphonium salts $[R_2CHO\overset{+}{S}(CH_3)_2]$. Baker (1965) has observed that in oxidation of some sugar derivatives with an axial substituent adjacent to the hydroxyl group, the equatorial epimer of the expected product is formed. Applications of these oxidation methods are illustrated below.

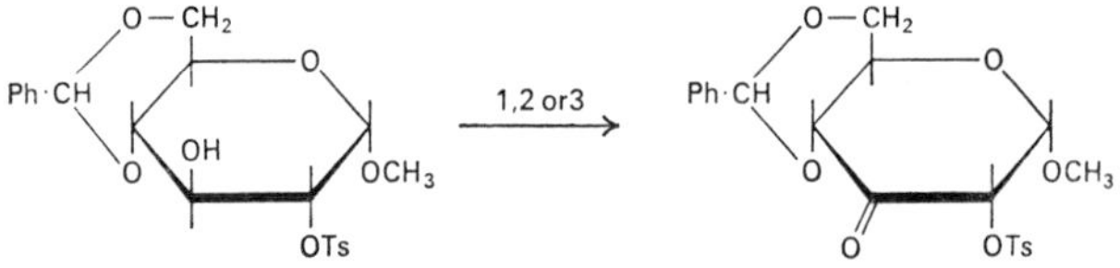

methyl 4,6-*O*-benzylidene-
2-*O*-tosyl-α-D-glucoside·

1,2 or 3

methyl 4,6-*O*-benzylidene-2-*O*-
tosyl-α-D-*ribo*hexosid-3-ulose

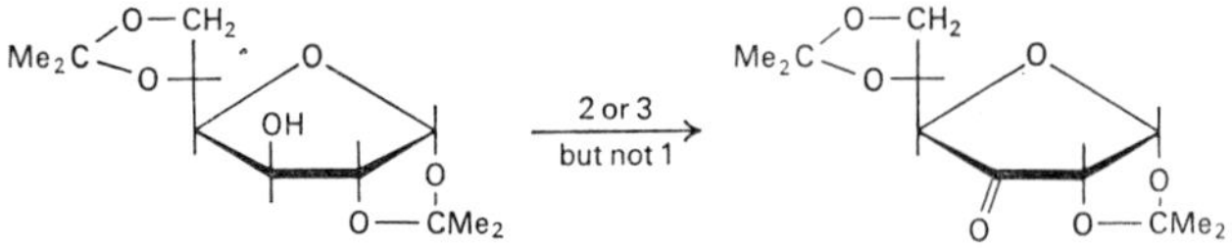

1,2:5,6-di-*O*-isopropylidene-
α-D-glucose

2 or 3
but not 1

1,2:5,6-di-*O*-isopropylidene-α-
D-*ribo*hexos-3-ulose

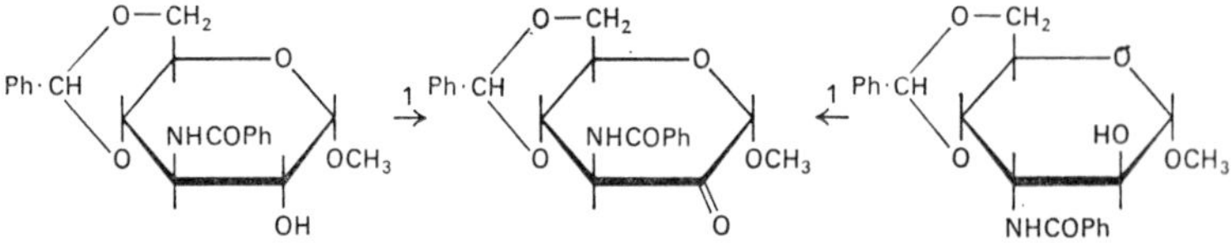

methyl 3-benzamido-
4,6-*O*-benzylidene-3-
deoxy-α-D-glucoside

methyl 3-benzamido-
4,6-*O*-benzylidene-3-
deoxy-α-D-*arabino*hexo-
sid-2-ulose

methyl 3-benzamido-
4,6-*O*-benzylidene-3-
deoxy-α-D-altroside

1. DMSO-DCC   2. DMSO-Ac₂o   3. DMSO-P₄O₁₀

Selective oxidation of sugar derivatives containing several free hydroxyl groups occurs with platinum and oxygen in neutral solution (Heyns 1962); axial hydroxyl groups are preferentially oxidized as shown below.

benzyl β-D-arabinopyranoside   benzyl β-D-*threo*pentosid-4-ulose

2. Unsaturated sugars

The importance of the unsaturated sugars lies in their use in syntheses and in the discovery of antibiotics containing derivatives of them or of vicinal dideoxy sugars (the corresponding saturated compounds).

Compounds have been synthesized in which a carbon–carbon double bond is part of the ring or in an open chain and also in which a triple bond is in a chain. We shall consider separately the two types of the first class, in which the double bond is attached to the reducing centre as in the so-called glycals (2) or located elsewhere in the ring, as in (3).

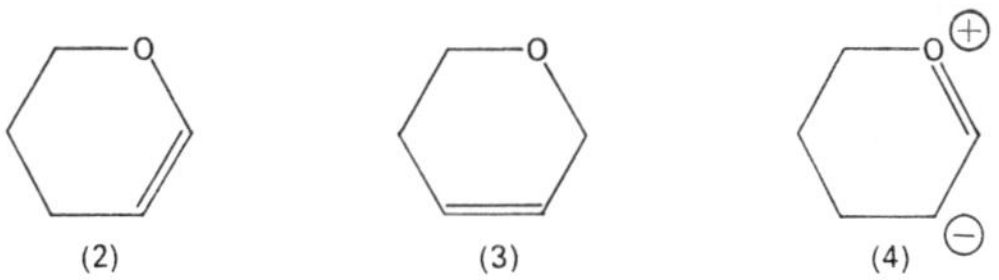

(2)   (3)   (4)

(a) *Glycals*

Reaction with zinc and acetic acid converts acetobromoaldoses into acetylated glycals, which can be de-acetylated by the usual methods (E. Fischer 1914, Helferich 1954).

The addition reactions of glycals are most useful, the direction of addition probably being governed by the contribution of the mesomeric form (4) favouring electrophilic attack at $C_{(2)}$.

Thus acid-catalysed addition of water and alcohols to a variety of glycals gives 2-deoxy derivatives. In the absence of acid the parent glycals are fairly stable but with their acetates addition occurs at $C_{(1)}$ with migration of the double bond to the $C_{(2)}$–$C_{(3)}$ position and displacement of the $C_{(3)}$–OAc group (Ferrier 1964), as shown below.

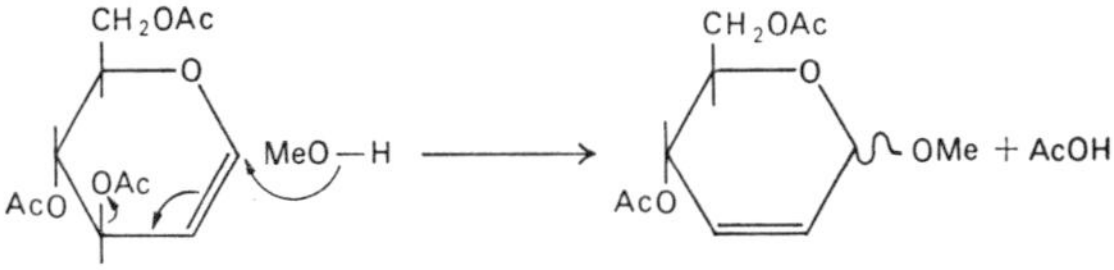

3,4,6-tri-*O*-acetyl - D - glucal   methyl 4,6-di-*O*-acetyl-2,3- dideoxy -
                                    D-*erythro* -hex-2-enosides

Hydroxylation of glycals with perbenzoic acid introduces hydroxyl groups at $C_{(1)}$ and $C_{(2)}$. The product from a glycal that has a free hydroxyl group on $C_{(3)}$ gives mainly *cis* 2,3-diols, whereas glycals substituted at $C_{(3)}$ give mainly *trans* 2,3-products. Thus, D-glucal gives D-mannose and only a trace of

D-glucose and D-galactal gives mostly D-talose but some D-galactose. However, D-glucal 3,4,6-triacetate gives mainly D-glucose 3,4,6-triacetate. These results have been interpreted as showing that in the $C_{(3)}$–OH compound, hydrogen-bonding stabilized the formation of the intermediate cis-epoxide on the same side of the ring as $C_{(3)}$, whereas the $C_{(3)}$–OAc group shields the double bond and the intermediate epoxide has the opposite configuration. Ring-opening of the epoxides occurs at $C_{(1)}$ to give the appropriate products.

(b) Other olefinic sugars

The best-known compounds in this class are those with the double bond between $C_{(2)}$ and $C_{(3)}$. Some of the wide variety of methods that have been used for their synthesis are illustrated below (see also (a) above). The most general method from cis

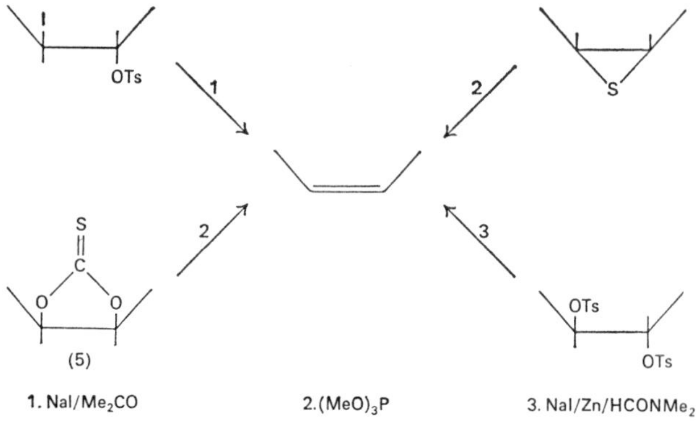

1. NaI/Me₂CO   2.(MeO)₃P   3. NaI/Zn/HCONMe₂

diol precursors is through the thionocarbonate (5) (Corey 1963, Haines 1965, Horton 1966). The reaction of vicinal disulphonates with zinc and sodium iodide in N,N-dimethylformamide (Tipson 1965) can be used with either cis or trans-diol precursors.

At the time of writing little work has been done on the addition reactions of sugars of this type.

Deoxy-sugars

Deoxy-sugars may be regarded as being derived from monosaccharides by replacing one or more hydroxyl groups by hydrogen atoms.

The 6-deoxy-aldohexoses occur widely in nature and include L-rhamnose (6-deoxy-L-mannose), L-fucose (6-deoxy-L-galactose), and D-quinovose (6-deoxy-D-glucose). Synthesis of 6-deoxyaldohexoses is best achieved by reducing with lithium

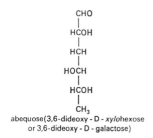

aluminium hydride the 6-bromo-6-deoxy-, 6-deoxy-6-iodo-, or 6-toluene-p-sulphonate of a suitably substituted derivative of the parent aldose (see also p. 61).

The reactions of the 6-deoxy-aldohexoses are the same as those of the corresponding aldohexose except where the primary hydroxyl group is involved in the latter. The 6-deoxy-aldohexoses form the sugar portion of the cardiac glycosides (digitalis glycosides), important as heart stimulants.

Some 3,6-dideoxyhexoses occur as components of the polysaccharides of *Salmonella* species. Those found include abequose, tyvelose, paratose, and colitose; these have the D-xylo, D-arabino, D-ribo, and L-xylo configurations, respectively.

$$
\begin{array}{c}
\text{CHO} \\
| \\
\text{HCOH} \\
| \\
\text{HCH} \\
| \\
\text{HOCH} \\
| \\
\text{HCOH} \\
| \\
\text{CH}_3
\end{array}
$$

abequose(3,6-dideoxy - D - *xylo*hexose or 3,6-dideoxy - D - galactose)

The most important 2-deoxyaldose is 2-deoxy-D-ribose (2-deoxy-D-*erythro*-pentose), which occurs widely as the sugar component of deoxyribonucleic acids (DNA) (see p. 74). It is best prepared by further degrading D-glucometasaccharinic acid obtained by the alkaline degradation of D-glucose (see p. 42).

Derivatives of 2-deoxy-aldose can be prepared from glycals as described above (p. 83).

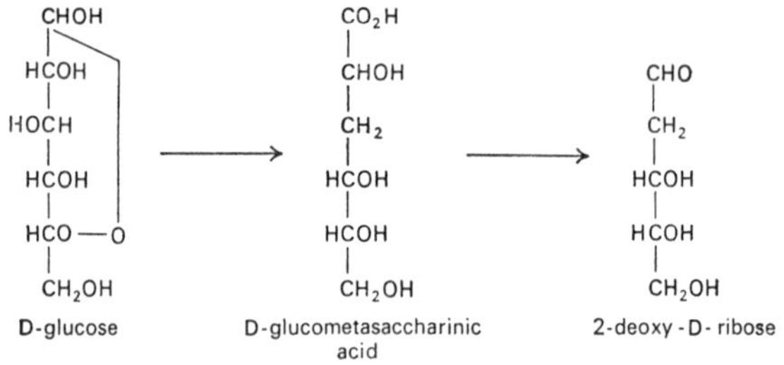

CHOH
|
HCOH ⌉
|
HOCH |
|
HCOH |
|
HCO ─── O
|
CH₂OH

D-glucose

⟶

CO₂H
|
CHOH
|
CH₂
|
HCOH
|
HCOH
|
CH₂OH

D-glucometasaccharinic
acid

⟶

CHO
|
CH₂
|
HCOH
|
HCOH
|
CH₂OH

2-deoxy-D-ribose

Another method for the preparation of deoxy-sugars is the reduction of epoxides with lithium aluminium hydride. For example, methyl 2,3-anhydro-4,6,O-benzylidene-a-D-alloside yields predominantly methyl 4,6-O-benzylidene-2-deoxy-a-D-altroside (diaxial opening) (Prins 1948).

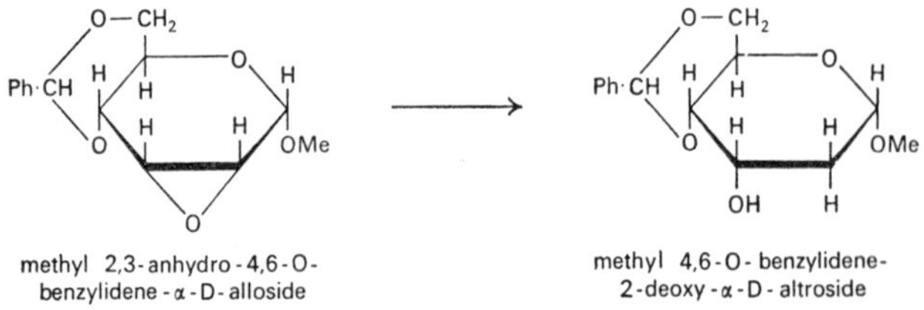

methyl 2,3-anhydro-4,6-O-
benzylidene-α-D-alloside

methyl 4,6-O-benzylidene-
2-deoxy-α-D-altroside

The 2-deoxy-aldoses react very rapidly with methanol in the presence of acids to yield the glycosides; these are hydrolysed to the free sugar more rapidly than the glycoside of the corresponding aldose.

Branched-chain sugars

A few sugars with a branched carbon chain occur naturally. Branching may be of the types (6) or (7), where R is a carbon function, generally CH₃, CH₂OH, or CHO, and replaces a hydroxyl group of a sugar as in (6) or a hydrogen atom as in (7).

H─C─R
|
(6)

HO─C─R
|
(7)

Examples of other naturally occurring branched-chain sugars are D-apiose (3-C-hydroxymethyl-D-*glycero*-aldotetrose) from the parsley plant, hamamelose (2-C-hydroxymethyl-D-ribose), from the bark of witch hazel, and streptose (5-deoxy-3-C-formyl-L-lyxose) a product of the degradation of the antibiotic, streptomycin.

D-apiose

hamamelose

streptose

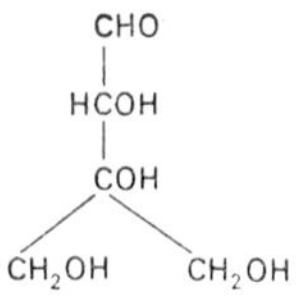

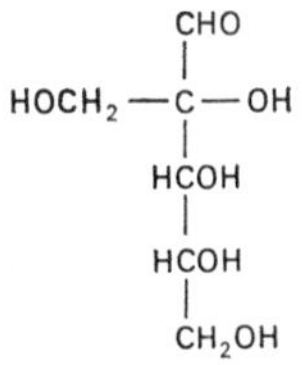

One of the best approaches to the synthesis of branched chain sugars is via carbonyl derivatives (see p. 8), either by direct attack with Grignard reagents and similar reagents or by treatment with diazomethane to give *spiro*epoxides that on opening will give branched derivatives, as shown schematically below (Overend 1954 on).

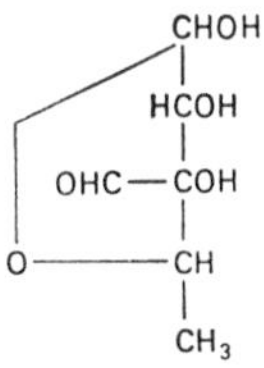

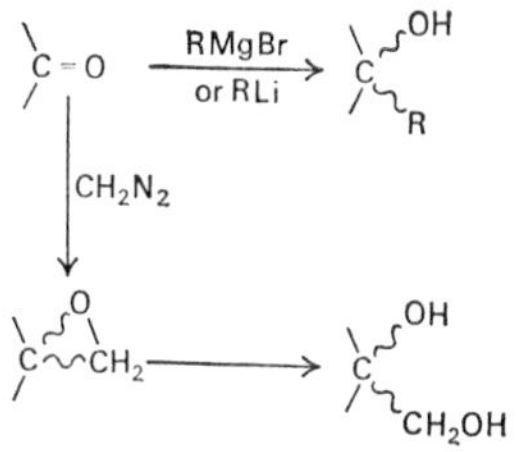

Polyols

The polyhydroxyalcohols comprise the acyclic polyols, also known as glycitols or alditols, and the cyclic polyols, often called cyclitols.

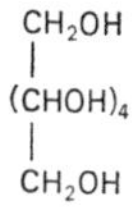

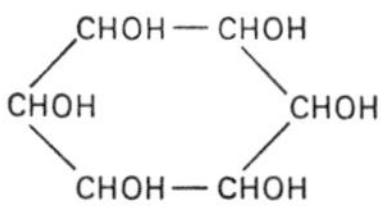

Because they do not have a reducing centre the polyols are not carbohydrates. However, they have many reactions in

hexitols

inositols
(cyclic hexitol)

common and are conveniently considered here. They form esters, ethers, acetals, and anhydro derivatives.

Alditols

The simplest alditol is generally considered to be glycerol (1,2,3-trihydroxypropane), occurring widely in the long-chain fatty esters of plant and animal oils and fats. The hexitols, mannitol and sorbitol, are found widely in plants but especially in seaweeds (mannitol) and the berries of the mountain ash (sorbitol).

Fewer stereoisomers exist than in the aldose series, because both ends of the carbon chain are identical. This also means that symmetrical, i.e. internally compensated or meso, forms are known; these are not optically active. Compared with eight aldopentoses there are only four stereoisomeric pentitols; ribitol (meso), xylitol (meso), and D-arabitol (D-lyxitol), and its enantiomorph.

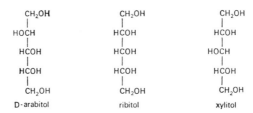

There are ten stereoisomeric hexitols compared with sixteen aldohexoses. Sorbitol (D-glucitol) is obtained commercially by electrolytic or catalytic reduction of D-glucose (see p. 5). Glycerol trinitrate ('nitroglycerin') and D-mannitol hexanitrate are important explosives and have also been used in the treatment of some heart diseases.

By studying the oxidation of mannitol, sorbitol, and dulcitol, with a limited amount of periodate it has been shown that attack occurs preferentially at the *threo* hydroxyl groups (Schwarz 1957).

Cyclitols

The most commonly studied cyclitols are the inositols or cyclohexanehexols. There are nine possible stereoisomers, each having a different arrangement of hydroxyl groups; all but two are optically inactive. They are shown below; each is named by a prefix before 'inositol', for example muco-inositol. Each will exist preferentially in the conformation with the greatest number of equatorial hydroxyl groups.

cis

epi

allo

neo

myo

muco

scyllo

dextro

laevo

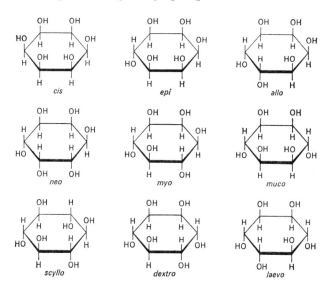

Inositols undergo many of the reactions described for carbohydrates. Reaction with acetone, in the presence of an acid catalyst, gives iso-propylidene derivatives, pairs of *cis*-hydroxyl groups generally being involved, though it is possible to have an isopropylidene group bridging a *trans* pair of hydroxyl groups (Angyal 1952). Inositol tosyl esters can give rise to anhydro inositols if *trans* to a free hydroxyl group.

Other important derivatives of the inositols are the deoxy-inositols (quercitols), the inososes (containing a keto group), and the inosamines (in which a hydroxyl group is replaced by amino).

cis-quercitol

epi-inosose

myo-inosamine-4

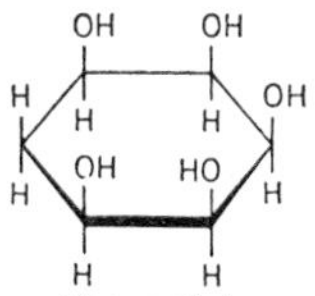

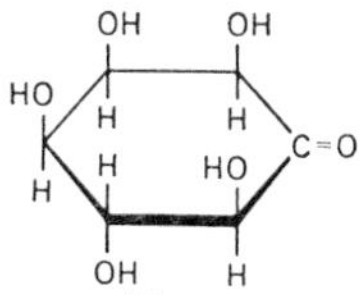

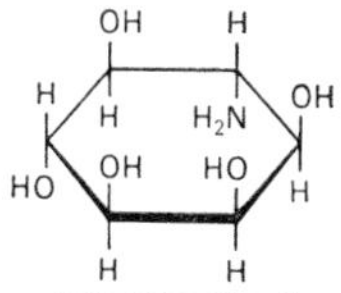

REVIEWS

Branched-chain sugars of natural occurrence, by F. Shafizadeh, *Adv. Carbohyd. Chem.* 1956, **11**, 263.

Cyclitols, by S. J. Angyal and L. Anderson, *Adv. Carbohyd. Chem.* 1959, **14**, 135.

Chemistry of the 2-deoxy sugars, by W. G. Overend and M. Stacey, *Adv. Carbohyd. Chem.* 1953, **8**, 45.

3,6-Dideoxyhexoses, by D. Westphal and O. Luderitz, *Angew. Chem.* 1960, **72**, 811 (in German).

Deoxy-sugars, by S. Hanessian, *Adv. Carbohyd. Chem.* 1966, **21**, 143.

Chemical and physical studies of cyclitols containing four or five hydroxyl groups, by G. E. McCasland, *Adv. Carbohyd. Chem.* 1965, **20**, 12.

Unsaturated sugars, by R. J. Ferrier, *Adv. Carbohyd. Chem.* 1965, **20**, 68.

Some approaches to the synthesis of rare sugars, by J. S. Brimacombe, *Chemistry in Britain* 1965, **2**, 99.

Recent developments in the chemistry of carbohydrates, by W. G. Overend, *Chem. Ind.* 1963, 342.

Dimethylsulphoxide oxidations, by W. W. Epstein and F. W. Sweat, *Chem. Rev.* 1967, **67**, 247.

12

ASCORBIC ACID

THE discovery was made 200 years ago that scurvy, the dreaded disease of sailors and explorers, could be prevented or cured by eating fresh green vegetables or by drinking fruit-juice. The first noteworthy step in the campaign to isolate the substance responsible for this antiscorbutic action was made when a more than usually active solution was prepared from lemon-juice (Zilva 1924). This concentrated solution was shown to be easily and reversibly oxidized-reduced without decomposition. The addition of alkali destroyed both the antiscorbutic and the reducing actions. A crystalline substance isolated from the cortex of the suprarenal glands (Szent-Gyorgyi 1928) was found to be identical with a substance obtained in very small amounts from cabbages, oranges, and lemons and, in better yield, from Hungarian red pepper, *Capsicum annum*. This crystalline material was shown to cure scurvy in guinea-pigs and was, in fact, the antiscorbutic factor or vitamin C.

The molecular formula was established as $C_6H_8O_6$ and, as the substance was wrongly considered to be a uronic acid, it was originally known as hexuronic acid. When the contention that it was a uronic acid was proved to be false, and when its identity with vitamin C was recognized, it was renamed L-ascorbic acid.

The chemical properties of ascorbic acid are summarized as follows.

1. It behaves as a weak acid that does not form a lactone.

2. It forms salts of the type $C_6H_7O_6M$ (i.e. one hydrogen atom has been replaced by an atom of a monovalent metal). This shows that ascorbic acid is not reacting as the lactone of the acid, $C_6H_{10}O_7$ (=$C_6N_8O_6$ + H_2O), because if it were the salts would have the formula $C_6H_9O_7M$. Hence, if it is a lactone, it is an exceedingly stable one.

3. If boiled with hydrochloric acid a quantitative yield of furfuraldehyde is obtained showing that at least five of the six carbon atoms form an unbranched chain.

4. Since ascorbic acid does not restore the colour to Schiff's

reagent, but gives an intense colour with aqueous ferric chloride, the substance may be considered to contain an enol group but not a free aldehyde group.

5. With phenylhydrazine and similar reagents a diphenyl-hydrazone (&c.) is obtained.

6. The action of aqueous iodine is a good example of the ease of the reversible oxidation.

$$C_6H_8O_6 + I_2 \rightleftarrows C_6H_6O_6 + 2HI$$

$$\underset{\text{acid}}{\underset{\text{ascorbic}}{}} \qquad \underset{\text{ascorbic acid}}{\underset{\text{dehydro-}}{}}$$

The action of iodine on dihydroxymaleic acid is similar.

$$\begin{array}{c}
CO_2H \\
| \\
C-OH \\
\| \\
C-OH \\
| \\
CO_2H \\
\text{dihydroxy-} \\
\text{maleic acid}
\end{array}
+ I_2 \rightleftarrows
\begin{array}{c}
CO_2H \\
| \\
C=O \\
| \\
C=O \\
| \\
CO_2H
\end{array}
+ 2HI$$

There is thus strong evidence for believing that the grouping —C(OH)=C(OH)— is present in ascorbic acid.

7. Dehydro-ascorbic acid is neutral in solution and behaves like the lactone of a polyhydroxy monobasic acid. Because of the ease and smoothness of the oxidation–reduction it is likely that ascorbic acid, too, is a lactone and that its acidity is due to the dissociation of one of the enolic hydroxyl groups (Hirst 1933).

8. With diazomethane a di-O-methylascorbic acid is obtained (diazomethane readily methylates acidic hydroxyl groups). Di-O-methylascorbic acid is a neutral substance which gives, with one equivalent of sodium hydroxide, a sodium salt *without loss* of a methyl group. This salt formation is similar to the opening of a lactone ring of the type:

$$\begin{array}{c}
CO \\
| \quad \diagdown \\
\vdots \\
| \\
MeO-C \\
\| \\
MeO-C \quad O \\
| \quad | \\
\text{di-O-methylascorbic} \\
\text{acid}
\end{array}
\rightarrow
\begin{array}{c}
CO_2Na \\
| \\
\vdots \\
| \\
MeO-C \\
\| \\
MeO-C \\
|
\end{array}$$

Part of the ascorbic acid molecule must be:

$$\begin{array}{c} CO \\ | \\ HO-C \\ \| \\ HO-C \quad O \\ | \quad | \end{array}$$

If ascorbic acid contained a carboxyl group, a methyl ester would be obtained with diazomethane. Reaction with sodium hydroxide solution would lead to a sodium salt but would be accompanied by the *loss* of a methyl group:

$$\underset{|}{CO_2H} \longrightarrow \underset{|}{CO_2Me} \longrightarrow \underset{|}{CO_2Na}$$

The lactone ring of ascorbic acid is more stable than that of the di-O-methyl derivative: the salts mentioned in (1) are of the form —C(OH)=C(OM)—.

9. Dehydro-ascorbic acid may be quantitatively oxidized with an equimolecular amount of sodium hypoiodite to oxalic acid and L-threonic acid. The latter was identified as the crystalline tri-O-methyl-L-threonamide. These products point to the presence in the reaction of 2,3-diketo-L-gulonic acid. This must be the acid of which dehydro-ascorbic acid is the lactone.

$$\begin{array}{ll}
\begin{array}{c}
CO_2H \\ | \\ CO \\ ----|---- \\ CO \\ | \\ H-C-OH \\ | \\ HO-C-H \\ | \\ CH_2OH \\
\text{2,3-diketo-L-} \\ \text{gulonic acid}
\end{array}
&
\longrightarrow
\quad
\begin{array}{cl}
CO_2H & \\ | & \text{oxalic acid} \\ CO_2H & \\ + & \\ CO_2H & \\ | & \\ H-C-OH & \text{L-threonic} \\ | & \text{acid} \\ HO-C-H & \\ | & \\ CH_2OH & \\ \downarrow & \\ CONH_2 & \\ | & \\ H-C-OMe & \\ | & \\ MeO-C-H & \\ | & \\ CH_2OMe & \\
\end{array}
\end{array}$$

tri-O-methyl-L-threonamide

10. Methylation by diazomethane, followed by further reaction with methyl iodide and silver oxide, gives tetra-O-methyl-ascorbic acid, which, on ozonolysis, yields *one* neutral substance

without loss of carbon atoms. This shows that tetra-O-methyl-ascorbic acid must contain a ring; otherwise the rupture of the carbon chain on ozonolysis would give two fragments. The position of the double bond in ascorbic acid is confirmed to be between $C_{(2)}$ and $C_{(3)}$ and the location of the ring determined by the examination of the neutral ozonolysis product (Hirst 1933).

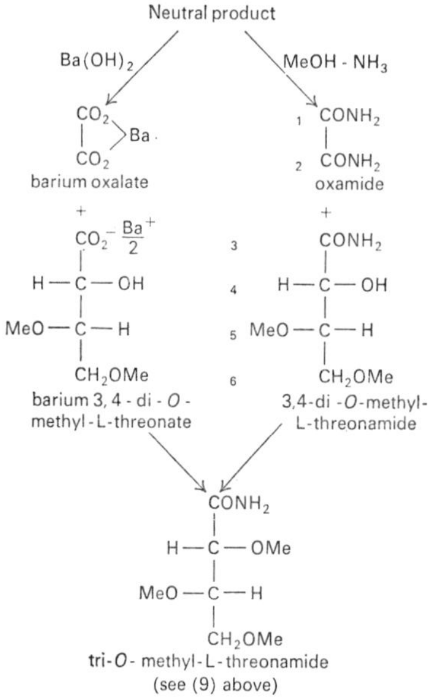

Neutral product

Ba(OH)$_2$ / \ MeOH - NH$_3$

CO$_2$
| >Ba·
CO$_2$
barium oxalate

1 CONH$_2$
|
2 CONH$_2$
oxamide

+

CO$_2^-$ $\frac{Ba^+}{2}$
|
H—C—OH
|
MeO—C—H
|
CH$_2$OMe
barium 3, 4 - di - O - methyl-L-threonate

+

3 CONH$_2$
|
4 H—C—OH
|
5 MeO—C—H
|
6 CH$_2$OMe
3,4-di -O-methyl-L-threonamide

CONH$_2$
|
H—C—OMe
|
MeO—C—H
|
CH$_2$OMe
tri-O- methyl-L-threonamide
(see (9) above)

The free hydroxyl group in 3,4-di-O-methyl-L-threonamide is shown to be on $C_{(2)}$ because this substance gives sodium cyanate under the conditions of the Weerman degradation (see p. 19): the amides of α-hydroxy acids, only, give this reaction. It follows that the ring in tetra-O-methyl-ascorbic acid must be attached to $C_{(4)}$. The structure of this compound has been completely elucidated.

CH$_2$OMe
+OMe—O
C=O
MeO   OMe
tetra -O- methyl-L- ascorbic acid

⟶

CH$_2$OMe
+OMe—O
C=O
C C
MeO O O OMe
'neutral product'

X-ray examination confirms this structure (Cox). The absorption spectra of ascorbic acid, its di-O-methyl derivative and dihydroxymaleic acid are all very similar, showing that they contain the same chromophore.

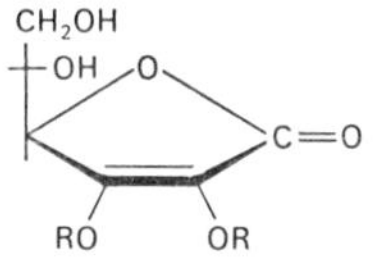

CH₂OH

L-ascorbic acid (R=H)
di-O-methyl-L-ascorbic acid (R=Me)

This constitution was confirmed by synthesis (Haworth and Hirst 1933). Aqueous calcium chloride and potassium cyanide were added to L-xylosone, obtained by the acid hydrolysis of L-xylosazone. The crystalline product isolated was imino ascorbic acid, which was readily converted by acid hydrolysis into L-ascorbic acid.

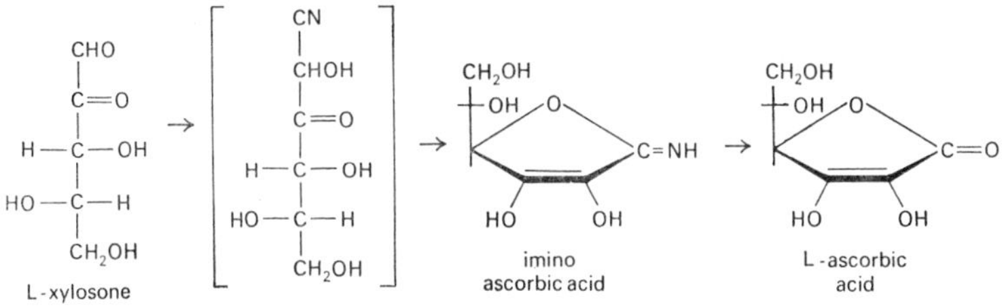

L-xylosone   imino   L-ascorbic
                      ascorbic acid   acid

A commercial method for preparing L-ascorbic acid for medicinal use is similar to a later synthesis (Reichstein 1934). D-Glucose is catalytically or electrolytically reduced to D-sorbitol which is bacterially oxidized (e.g. with *Bacterium xylinum*) to L-sorbose. Careful treatment with nitric acid gives a fair yield of 2-keto-L-gulonic acid. A better method is to prepare di-O-isopropylidene-L-sorbose, so protecting the other alcohol groups, and oxidize this compound with permanganate. Acid hydrolysis removes the acetone residues and leaves 2-keto-L-gulonic acid. If the methyl ester of this acid is treated with sodium methoxide, enolization takes place. Acid hydrolysis leads to the stable γ-lactone, L-ascorbic acid.

SYNTHESIS OF L-ASCORBIC ACID

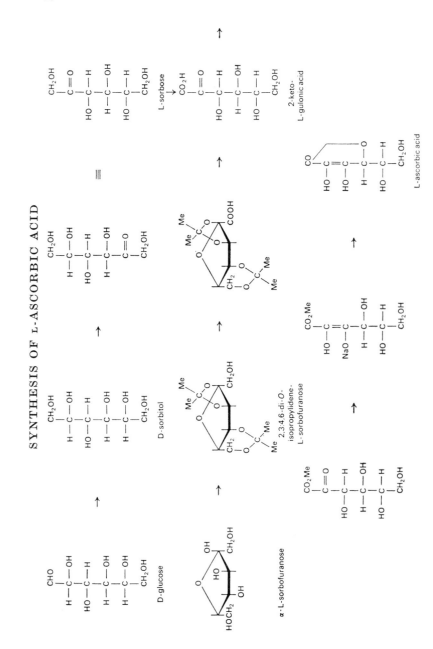

By similar methods but starting from different sugars analogues of vitamin C have been prepared. None has been found to have as high antiscorbutic activity as L-ascorbic acid.

REVIEW

Analogs of ascorbic acid, by F. Smith, *Adv. Carbohyd. Chem.* 1947, **2**, 79.

13

DI-, TRI-, AND TETRA-SACCHARIDES

ALL the sugars considered in this chapter are sweet-tasting, crystalline, and soluble in water. Of the disaccharides, only two, sucrose and lactose, are found abundantly in nature. Sucrose, the well-known foodstuff, is the sugar of plants, found in beet and cane, the commerical sources. Lactose is the sugar that occurs in mammalian milk. Maltose, found free in nature to a limited extent (e.g. in soya beans), is usually prepared from starch by enzymic hydrolysis. Cellobiose is obtained by the graded hydrolysis of cellulose. The trisaccharides, raffinose, melezitose, and gentianose, are all found in nature. Stachyose is a crystalline tetrasaccharide found in the roots of *Stachys tuberifera*.

Disaccharides

The disaccharides are glycosides, which explains their ready hydrolysis by dilute acid. Earlier systems of nomenclature were based on this attitude to their structure but they are now named as monosubstituted sugars. The right-hand residue of the disaccharide (1) is considered the fundamental unit for naming, as it has its reducing centre unsubstituted. Sugar (1) is a 4-O-substituted-D-glucopyranose. The substituent on the 4-position is

(1)

the α-D-mannopyranosyl group and so (1) is 4-O-(α-D-mannopyranosyl)-D-glucopyranose. If both monosaccharide units are joined through their reducing centres, the resultant disaccharide will be non-reducing. Nomenclature for such disaccharides is based on considering either monosaccharide as the basic unit, the other as a glycosidic substituent. Consider, for example,

sugar (2), which could be named either β-D-glucopyranosyl-α-D-mannopyranoside or α-D-mannopyranosyl-β-D-glucopyranoside.
No numbers need to be included in the names of such disaccharides since the nomenclature makes it clear that the reducing

(2)

(The right-hand sugar unit (D -glucosyl)
is drawn upside down for convenience)

groups of both units are involved. A shortened notation may be used for di-, tri-, and higher saccharides. This uses the first three letters of the sugar names, except for glucose (G), p for pyranose and f for furanose, and the appropriate numbers to denote the linkages. Thus sugar (1) is α-D-Man$p$ 1——4 D-Gp.

The normal procedure for determining the structure of a disaccharide may be summarized as follows.

1. Determination of whether the disaccharide is reducing or not.

2. Acid hydrolysis leads to two monosaccharide molecules, which are identified.

3. Consideration of the specific rotation together with enzymic studies determines whether the glycosidic link is α or β. Maltase and emulsin (see p. 24) are widely used for this.

4. Complete methylation followed by hydrolysis with acid leads to two methylated monosaccharides. These may be separated by high vacuum distillation, or by gas–liquid or column chromatography, and identified. This shows which sugar, if any, forms the reducing unit of the disaccharide molecule and at which carbon atom it is substituted by the other sugar unit. The ring structure of both parts *may* also be proved. However, in some cases this method gives ambiguous results as it does not distinguish between an aldohexopyranose substituted on $C_{(4)}$ and an aldohexofuranose substituted on $C_{(5)}$. The necessary extra stage is described in detail for cellobiose.

The application of these methods is illustrated in the examples that follow.

CONSTITUTION OF CELLOBIOSE

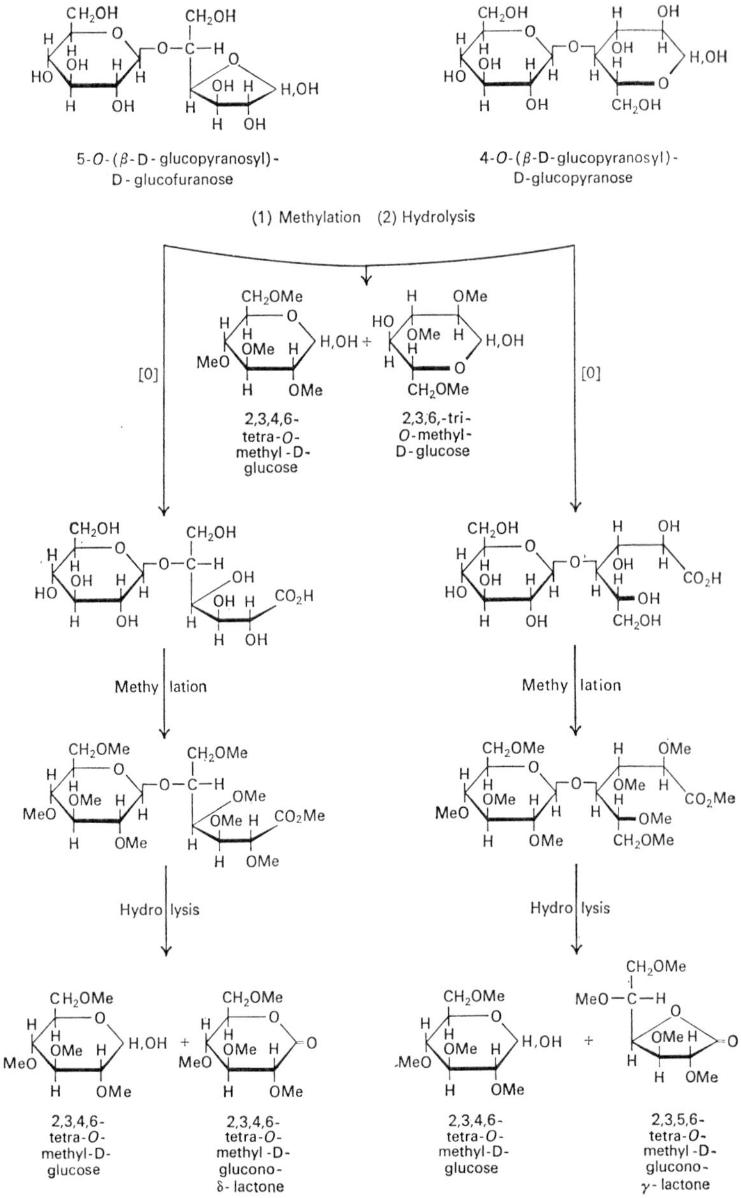

5-O-(β-D-glucopyranosyl)-
D-glucofuranose

4-O-(β-D-glucopyranosyl)-
D-glucopyranose

(1) Methylation   (2) Hydrolysis

[0]

2,3,4,6-
tetra-O-
methyl-D-
glucose

2,3,6,-tri-
O-methyl-
D-glucose

[0]

Methylation

Methylation

Hydrolysis

Hydrolysis

2,3,4,6-
tetra-O-
methyl-D-
glucose

2,3,4,6-
tetra-O-
methyl-D-
glucono-
δ-lactone

2,3,4,6-
tetra-O-
methyl-D-
glucose

2,3,5,6-
tetra-O-
methyl-D-
glucono-
γ-lactone

Cellobiose is readily obtained in crystalline form by the careful hydrolysis of cellulose. Its structure has been elucidated by applying the general methods (Haworth 1927).

1. Its solutions mutarotate, it reduces Fehling's solution, and it forms an osazone. These properties show that one of the monosaccharide units has a free reducing group.

2. Acid hydrolysis gives two molecules of D-glucose.

3. It is hydrolysed by emulsin, but not by maltase. Thus cellobiose is an O-(β-D-glucosyl)-D-glucose.

4. Methylation gives an octamethyl derivative, methyl hepta-O-methyl-cellobioside, which is hydrolysed to 2,3,4,6-tetra-O-methyl-D-glucose, 2,3,6-tri-O-methyl-D-glucose, and methanol. The first product shows that the glucosidic part is pyranoid and the second that the other glucose residue is either pyranoid linked through $C_{(4)}$ or furanoid linked through $C_{(5)}$.

5. Oxidation with bromine water gives cellobionic acid. This on methylation, followed by hydrolysis, gives 2,3,4,6-tetra-O-methyl-D-glucose and 2,3,5,6-tetra-O-methyl-D-glucono-γ-lactone (see p. 100).

This proves cellobiose to be 4-O-(β-D-glucopyranosyl)-D-glucopyranose.

CELLOBIOSE

This structure has been confirmed by synthesis. In one method acetobromoglucose and β-D-glucopyranose 1,2,3,6-tetra-acetate (prepared from the 1,2,3,4-tetra-acetate by acetyl migration; p. 56) are condensed to give cellobiose octa-acetate (Stacey 1946). Deacetylation with sodium in methanol gives cellobiose.

Sucrose is the commonest sugar known and is obtained mainly from the sugar cane; in temperate zones, it is manufactured from a specially bred beetroot that contains from 15 to 20 per cent of the sugar.

The structure of sucrose has been deduced in the following manner.

It does not reduce Fehling's solution, nor react with phenylhydrazine, nor do its solutions mutarotate. This shows that the consitutent sugars are linked through their reducing centres. Treatment with acids converts sucrose ($[a]_D + 66°$) into an equimolecular mixture of D-glucose ($[a]_D + 52°$) and D-fructose ($[a]_D - 92°$). Because of the high negative rotation of fructose, the final mixture is laevorotatory ($[a]_D - 20°$). For this reason this hydrolysis is often called the inversion of sucrose and the glucose–fructose mixture referred to as invert sugar. The same hydrolysis is achieved by the enzyme invertase that is found in yeast, plants, and animal digestive systems.

Sucrose is hydrolysed by maltase, so the glucose part probably has the a configuration. The kinetics of hydrolysis and the optical rotation give strong evidence for believing that the glucose part is a and the fructose part β. Thus sucrose is an a-D-glucosyl β-D-fructoside, or, alternatively, a β-D-fructosyl a-D-glucoside.

Methylation followed by hydrolysis gives 2,3,4,6-tetra-O-methyl-D-glucose and a dextrorotatory tetra-O-methyl-D-fructose, shown by oxidation reactions to be the 1,3,4,6-derivative. Thus sucrose is a-D-glucopyranosyl β-D-fructofuranoside, or, alternatively, β-D-fructofuranosyl a-D-glucopyranoside.

SUCROSE

In this the fructofuranose unit (see p. 32) has been rotated though 180° about an axis passing through the oxygen atom and midway between $C_{(3)}$ and $C_{(4)}$.

Sucrose octa-acetate has been synthesized in 5 per cent yield from the reaction of 1,2-anhydro-a-D-glucopyranose 3,4,6-triacetate with D-fructofuranose 1,3,4,6-tetra-acetate in a sealed tube at 100° (Lemieux 1956). This is added proof that sucrose is an a-D-glucoside since the reaction of the above 1,2-anhydro-D-glucose derivative is known to yield a-D-glucosides (see later). An enzymic synthesis was achieved by treating D-glucose 1-phosphate with D-fructose in the presence of an enzyme obtained from *Pseudomonas saccharophilia* (Hassid and Doudoroff 1944).

Other disaccharides

The structures of some other disaccharides, proved in a similar manner to those described above, are summarized in the table.

Disaccharide	Source	Structure
Trehalose	Fungi, yeasts	a-D-glucopyranosidyl-a-D-glucopyranose
Sophorose	Hydrolysis of a glyco-side from *Sophora japonica*	2-O-(β-D-glucopyranosyl)-D-glucopyranose
Turanose	Partial hydrolysis of melezitose	3-O-(a-D-glucopyranosyl)-D-fructose
Laminaribiose	Partial hydrolysis of laminarin from seaweeds	3-O-(β-D-glucopyranosyl)-D-glucopyranose
Maltose	Enzymic hydrolysis of starch	4-O-(a-D-glucopyranosyl)-D-glucopyranose
Lactose	Whey	4-O-(β-D-galactopyranosyl)-D-glucopyranose
Isomaltose	Enzymic hydrolysis of amylopectin	6-O-(a-D-glucopyranosyl)-D-glucopyranose
Gentiobiose	Partial hydrolysis of gentianose	6-O-(β-D-glucopyranosyl)-D-glucopyranose
Melibiose	Partial hydrolysis of raffinose	6-O-(a-D-galactopyranosyl)-D-glucopyranose

The disaccharides with β-linkages can be synthesized by the Koenigs–Knorr method (see p. 54). Synthesis of a-linked disaccharides is not so easy. One method is to use a halogeno sugar with a group on $C_{(2)}$, such as nitrate, that has no neighbouring group effect. For example, 3,4,6-tri-O-acetyl-β-D-glucosyl chloride 2-nitrate condenses with 1,2,3,4-tetra-O-acetyl-D-glucose to give a good yield of isomaltose (a-linkage) and a small amount of gentiobiose (β-linkage) (Wolfrom 1961).

A second method involves use of 1,2-anhydro-D-glucose 3,4,6-triacetate at elevated temperatures (ordinary temperatures cause β-D-glucoside formation). The course of the reaction is illustrated above where ROH is a sugar derivative suitably substituted to leave free only the appropriate hydroxyl group (Lemieux 1953). Maltose has been synthesized by this method using β-D-glucose 1,2,3,6-tetra-acetate as the alcohol, ROH.

Trisaccharides

Raffinose is the most abundant trisaccharide found in nature. It occurs in the mother liquors from sugar-beet crystallization and as a crystalline exudation on certain eucalyptus trees. The constitution of this trisaccharide is elucidated by hydrolysis experiments. Dilute acid gives equimolecular proportions of D-glucose, D-galactose, and D-fructose. Treatment with invertase affords D-fructose and melibiose whereas α-galactosidase, an enzyme which specifically breaks the α-galactoside link, leads to D-galactose and sucrose. Thus, the raffinose molecule is made up of D-glucose and D-galactose linked as in melibiose with the D-fructose linked to D-glucose as in sucrose. This has been confirmed by methylation studies. Raffinose is thus *O-α-D-galactopyranosyl-(1 → 6)-O-α-D-glucopyranosyl-(1 → 2) β-D-fructofuranoside* (or α-D-Gal*p* 1——6 α-D-G*p* 1——2 β-D-Fru*f*).

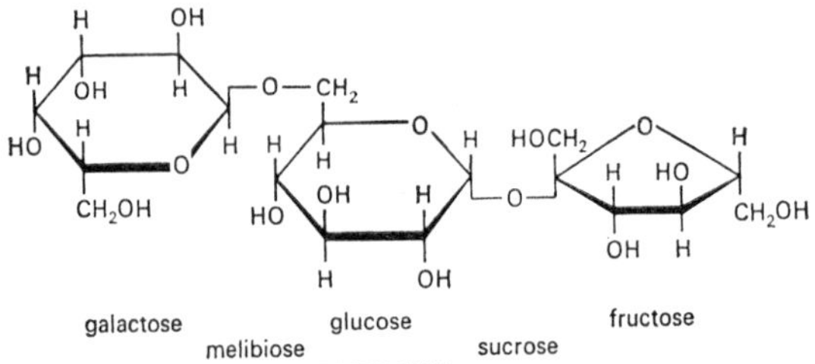

galactose   glucose   fructose
      melibiose   sucrose
          RAFFINOSE

Gentianose, another non-reducing trisaccharide, obtained from gentian roots, had its structure determined by the methods used

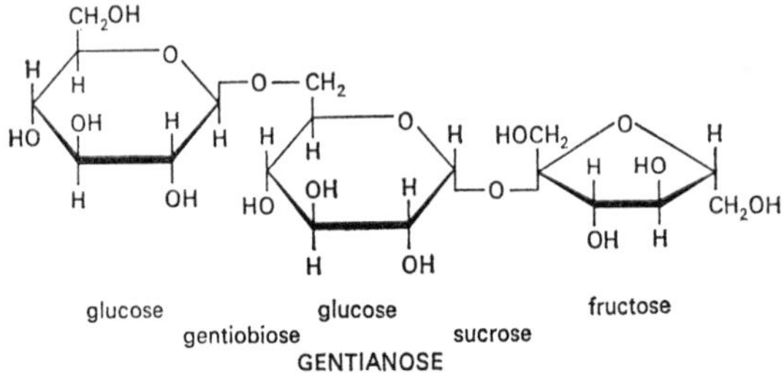

glucose   glucose   fructose
      gentiobiose   sucrose
          GENTIANOSE

for raffinose. Gentianose is O-β-D-glucopyranosyl-$(1 \rightarrow 6)$-O-α-D-glucopyranosyl-$(1 \rightarrow 2)$ β-D-fructofuranoside (or β-D-Gp 1——6 α-D-Gp 1——2 β-D-Fru$f$).

Melezitose is found in the 'honey-dew' of many trees such as the lime. Its structure has been proved by methods similar to those above to be O-α-D-glucopyranosyl-$(1 \rightarrow 3)$-O-β-D-fructofuranosyl-$(2 \rightarrow 1)$ α-D-glucopyranoside (or α-D-Gp 1——3 β-D-Fru$f$ 2——1 α-D-Gp).

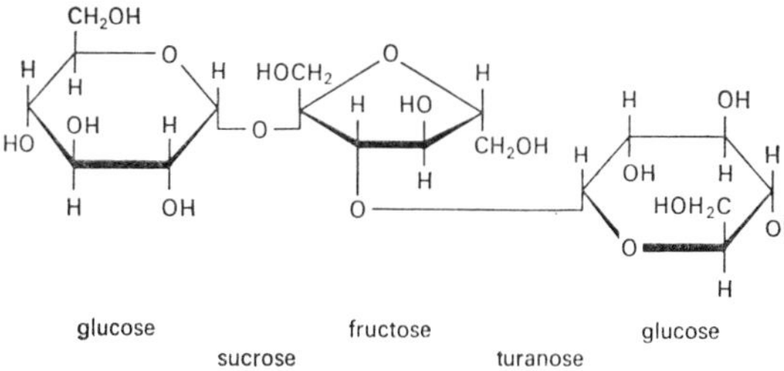

glucose   fructose   glucose
         sucrose   turanose
            MELEZITOSE

Tetrasaccharides

Stachyose, which occurs in the roots of several plant species, yields sucrose and raffinose on enzymic hydrolysis. Methylation and hydrolysis gives 2,3,4,6-tetra-O-methyl-D-galactose, 2,3,4-tri-O-methyl-D-galactose, 2,3,4-tri-O-methyl-D-glucose, and 1,3, 4,6-tetra-O-methyl-D-fructose. This means that stachyose is O-α-D-galactopyranosyl-$(1 \rightarrow 6)$-O-α-D-galactopyranosyl-$(1 \rightarrow 6)$-O-α-D-glucopyranosyl-$(1 \rightarrow 2)$ β-D-fructofuranoside (or α-D-Gal$p$ 1——6 α-D-Gal$p$ 1——6 α-D-Gp 1——2 β-D-Fru$f$).

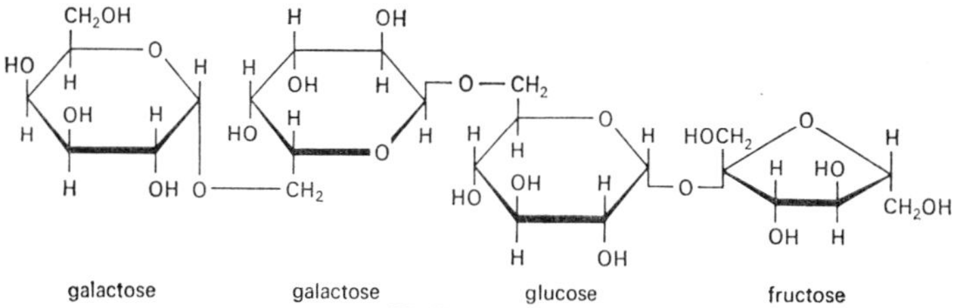

galactose   galactose   glucose   fructose
                    STACHYOSE

REVIEWS

Structure and configuration of sucrose, by I. Levi and C. B. Purves, *Adv. Carbohyd. Chem.* 1949, **4**, 1.

Enzymatic synthesis of sucrose and other disaccharides, by Z. Hassid and M. Doudoroff, *Adv. Carbohyd. Chem.* 1950, **5**, 29.

Synthesis of oligosaccharides, by W. L. Evans, D. D. Reynolds, and E. A. Tolley, *Adv. Carbohyd. Chem.* 1951, **6**, 27.

Lactose, by J. R. Clamp, L. Hough, J. L. Hickson, and R. L. Whistler, *Adv. Carbohyd. Chem.* 1961, **16**, 159.

Oligosaccharides, by R. W. Bailey and J. B. Pridham, *Adv. Carbohyd. Chem.* 1962, **17**, 121.

The oligosaccharides, by R. W. Bailey (Pergamon Press, Oxford, 1965).

The oligosaccharides, by J. Staněk, M. Černý, and J. Pacák (Academic Press, New York, 1965).

14

POLYSACCHARIDES

THE polysaccharides have a very wide distribution in nature. Some, such as cellulose and chitin, are found as the skeletal material of plants and animals, while others, like starch and glycogen, occur as reserve substances, readily convertible as required into energy.

Because polysaccharides are all compounds of high molecular weight they have the properties generally associated with colloids. The polysaccharide molecule is made up from a large number of simple sugar molecules, which are linked together glycosidically as in the oligosaccharides described in the previous chapter. The polyuronic acids or polyuronides are an important group of polysaccharides in which the sugar units are replaced by uronic acids.

Some polysaccharides have linear molecules with all the sugar units linked in one unbranched chain, whereas others have branched molecules containing a main chain to which smaller chains are linked glycosidically. Some polysaccharides have a highly branched structure.

Before studying its structure a polysaccharide has generally to be isolated from its source; this must be done with the minimum of degradation. The homogeneity of the resultant product has to be established to ensure that it is not a mixture of polysaccharides.

General methods of structural study

When studying the structure of an unknown polysaccharide several problems arise: how many constituent monosaccharides does it contain and, if more than one, in what order are they linked; has it a branched or linear structure; are the rings pyranose, furanose, or some of each; are the glycosidic links α or β or a mixture thereof; what is the molecular weight of the polysaccharide?

Before individual polysaccharides are considered the general methods used for elucidating structures will be described.

1. *Acid hydrolysis.* Hydrolysis of a polysaccharide will break it down into its constituent monosaccharides, which may be identified. Careful partial hydrolysis will sometimes yield di-, tri-, and higher oligosaccharides as products. These give information about the mode of linkage of the individual monosaccharides and also of their ring size. Care in interpretation is required, however, for under acid conditions it is possible for the liberated monosaccharides to recombine in a manner different from that in the polysaccharide ('reversion', see p. 41).

2. *Acetolysis.* This involves treatment of the polysaccharide with acetic anhydride containing 3 to 5 per cent sulphuric acid. Whereas the 1,6-link is the most resistant to acid hydrolysis, it is the least stable to acetolysis. These two reactions can therefore lead to different fragments from the same polysaccharide.

3. *Methylation.* As with disaccharides, the complete methylation of a polysaccharide followed by hydrolysis yields partially methylated monosaccharides, which may identify the ring size in the sugar units of the polysaccharide as well as show their point of linkage. Again, pyranose units linked through $C_{(4)}$ will not be distinguished from furanose ones linked through $C_{(5)}$ (see p. 99).

4. *Smith degradation* (1952). Reduction with sodium borohydride of a periodate-oxidized polysaccharide followed by acid hydrolysis gives fragments that show the mode of linkage present in the original polysaccharide. Examples are shown below for some of the possibilities.

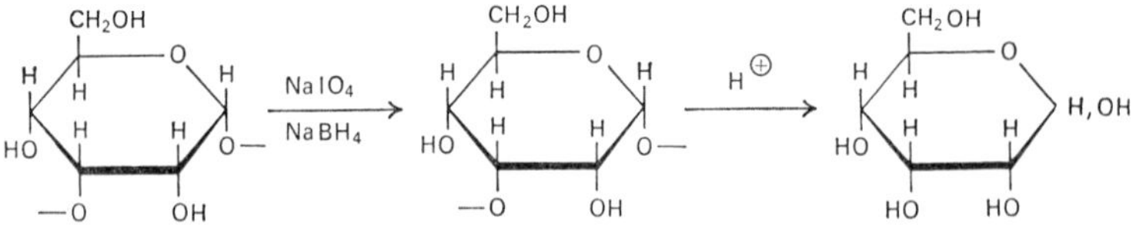

| 1 → 3 link | (no oxidation) | unattacked sugar unit |

| 1 → 4 link | | erythritol | glycolaldehyde |

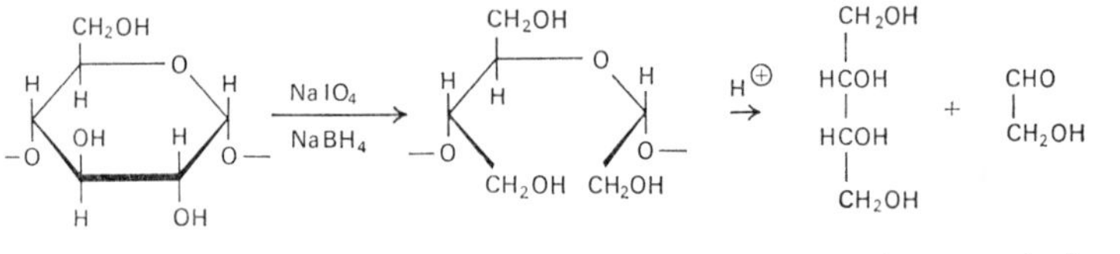

$1 \rightarrow 6$ link   glycerol   glycol
                                                                     aldehyde

The other problem involved in polysaccharide structure is the determination of the number of units making up a molecule. Physical methods, such as viscosity measurements, are most reliable, although chemical methods have been used. Typical ones are described under cellulose and starch.

CELLULOSE

Cellulose is the polysaccharide that forms the main constituent of the cell walls of plants. The seed hairs of the cotton plant are almost pure cellulose. The longer fibres are used for spinning into cloth, while the short hairs (linters) are the main source of cellulose for chemical purposes. Other materials that contain large amounts of cellulose are wood (average cellulose content, about 50 per cent), bast fibres such as flax (80 per cent) and jute (65 per cent), leaf fibres such as hemp (80 per cent), and cereal straws (45 per cent).

The impurities of cotton cellulose total about 2 per cent and consist mainly of the protective film of wax, oil from the seed, pectic substances, mineral substances such as sand, and a trace of colouring matter. The purification requires careful control to avoid degradation of the cellulose molecule. After mechanical cleaning to eliminate gross impurities such as stones and leaves (ginning), the linters are boiled with dilute aqueous sodium hydroxide in an inert atmosphere to remove pectin, wax, and oil. After bleaching with dilute sodium hypochlorite the material contains about 99·7 per cent pure cellulose, the residue being mainly silica.

Cellulose made from wood is chiefly used for paper manufacture, but is also used in fibre production (see p. 115).

The purification processes, although relatively mild, do cause some hydrolysis of the cellulose. By varying the times occupied by the various purification processes, forms of cellulose may be obtained differing widely in the average size of the molecule. A rough classification is given by solubility. The most generally useful type, a-cellulose, has not been seriously degraded and is not soluble in 17·5 per cent aqueous sodium hydroxide. Material soluble in this solution, but insoluble in dilute acid, is known as β-cellulose: γ-cellulose, which is soluble in both, has a low molecular weight. The importance of knowing the life-history of a given sample of cellulose is emphasized: it is wrong to believe that the properties of cellulosic material are necessarily those of pure, undegraded cellulose. Furthermore, results obtained will always be average values, for any sample of the polysaccharide will contain molecules covering a range of molecular weights.

The high molecular weight of undegraded cellulose is shown by its colloidal properties. The fact that it swells in certain solvents is sufficient to prove it is a high polymer. One of the best solvents is cuprammonium hydroxide in which it swells rapidly and then dissolves to form a viscous solution. If air is rigorously excluded, degradation of the cellulose is slight: if the solution is gradually added in a thin stream to a large excess of water, the cellulose is regenerated in the form of a thin thread, usually known as 'cuprammonium rayon'. The adsorbing and swelling properties of cellulose are also displayed by its behaviour in aqueous sodium hydroxide (e.g. 20 per cent solution). If after a few minutes in such a solution the cellulose is washed free of alkali, it is found to have increased capacity for dyes and greater tensile strength (Mercer 1850); it is said to have been 'mercerized'.

Constitution of cellulose

1. Elementary analysis indicated a formula of $C_6H_{10}O_5$.
2. Acid hydrolysis of cellulose gave almost theoretical yields of pure crystalline D-glucose (Flechsig 1883, Monier-Williams 1921).
3. Acetylation, followed by hydrolysis with methanolic hydrogen chloride, gave almost theoretical yields of crystalline methyl D-glucosides (Irvine 1922).
4. Acetylation gave a triacetate; nitration a trinitrate.
5. Methylation of cellulose with dimethyl sulphate and aque-

ous sodium hydroxide, followed by hydrolysis with methanolic hydrogen chloride, gave a high yield (86 per cent) of methyl 2,3,6-tri-O-methyl-D-glucosides (Irvine and Hirst 1923).

6. When subjected to acetolysis (i.e. simultaneous hydrolysis and acetylation) cellulose gave cellobiose octa-acetate (50 per cent yield). It was shown that D-glucose was not converted into this compound by the acetolysis mixture; indeed, cellobiose octa-acetate was itself broken down in the reaction mixture used. Thus the yield obtained was high enough to justify the belief that cellulose was made up of cellobiose units (Franchimont 1879, Freudenberg 1921).

The above results, together with the colloidal nature of cellulose, show that it is a large molecule made up of D-glucose units joined together as in cellobiose, i.e. of β-D-glucose units linked glycosidically from $C_{(1)}$ to $C_{(4)}$. The fact that it forms threads when regenerated under suitable conditions is evidence that the molecule is linear. These results have been further proved by use of the Smith degradation on periodate-oxidized cellulose, which gave almost exclusively D-erythritol and glycolaldehyde. In addition to cellobiose, higher saccharides, from cellotriose (the trisaccharide built up from three β-1,4-linked D-glucose units) to celloheptaose, have been isolated from the products obtained by the gentle acid hydrolysis of cellulose (Zechmeister 1931, Miller 1960).

Cellulose from many different sources has been examined by the above methods and in all cases the results have been identical.

Molecular weight of cellulose

All the chemical methods that have been used are based on the determination of the proportion of end-groups compared with the total number of units in the molecule. In the formula on p. 112 it can be seen that one end-group is reducing, the other non-reducing. The 'end-group assay' methods use one or other or both of these.

The earliest method was based on determining the reducing power of cellulose towards Fehling's solution (Bergmann 1930). The results are always low because some of the hydroxyl groups are oxidized, as well as $C_{(1)}$ of the reducing end-group.

Another widely used method consists of *complete* methylation

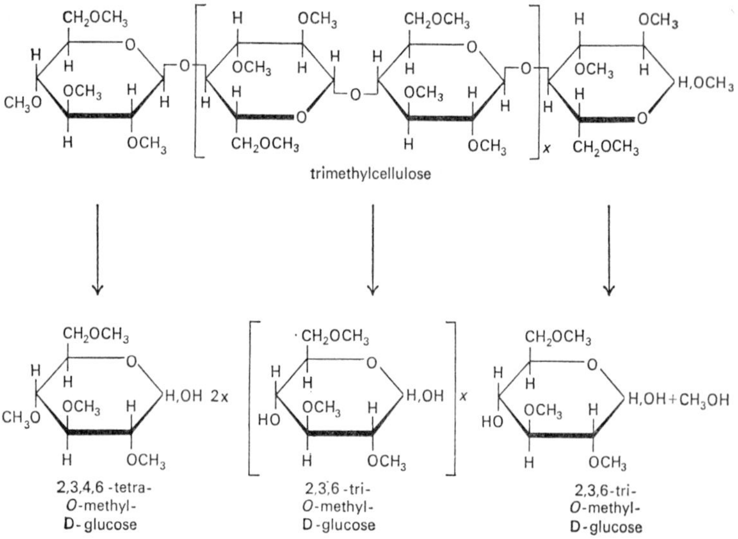
trimethylcellulose
2,3,4,6-tetra-O-methyl-D-glucose
2,3,6-tri-O-methyl-D-glucose
2,3,6-tri-O-methyl-D-glucose

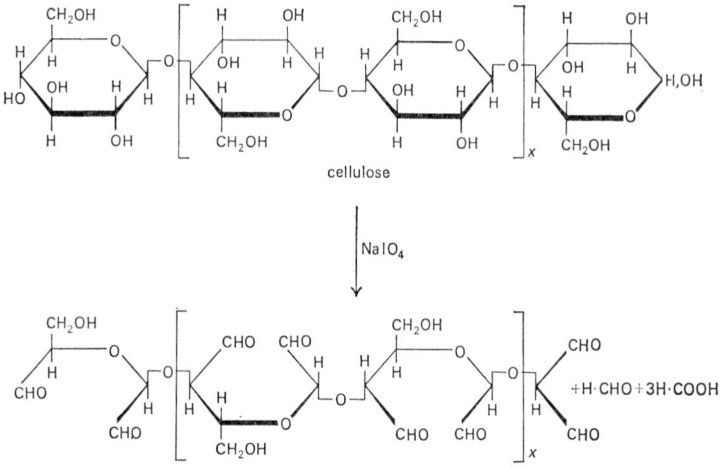
cellulose
NaIO4
+H·CHO+3H·COOH

in an inert atmosphere, followed by hydrolysis with dilute acid to break all the glycosidic links (Haworth 1932). Thus each molecule of cellulose will give one molecule of 2,3,4,5-tetra-O-methyl-D-glucose from the non-reducing end, together with a large number of molecules of 2,3,6-tri-O-methyl-D-glucose. The original method of separating the tetra-O-methyl derivative was high vacuum distillation: this method has been improved by the use of efficient fractionating columns (Hibbert 1942). Other separation methods have also been employed, notably chromatography (Bell 1944; Jones 1944, 1949; Hirst 1947, 1949). Once the proportion of tetra-O-methyl to tri-O-methyl-D-glucose has been determined, the chain-length may be calculated. The results obtained by this method correspond to a chain-length of 100–200 D-glucose residues, but are minimum values since it is impossible to methylate cellulose completely without degradation.

A third method that has been used is based on periodate oxidation (Hirst 1945). It has been found that oxidation with sodium periodate usually goes too far, but with saturated solutions of the less soluble potassium metaperiodate, oxidation takes place smoothly and follows the general course already described (see p. 68). Study of the cellulose formula shows that only the two end-groups yield formic acid, three molecules of the acid being formed from each cellulose chain (see formulae on previous page); the acid is estimated by titration. The results indicate that cellulose has a chain-length of about 1000 D-glucose units. The method is liable to error because of 'over-oxidation' (non-specific oxidation) in which the reducing end-group dialdehyde (1) may be further oxidized at the activated CH group to yield additional formic acid. This error is overcome by extrapolation.

Several physical methods have been used for determining the molecular weight of high polymers. These methods have been applied to cellulose. The principal methods used have been ultracentrifuging (Kraemer 1934) and determination of viscosity of cuprammonium solutions (Staudinger 1930). The values obtained for native cellulose by these methods were about 2000 and 2000 to 3000 D-glucose units respectively.

The results obtained by the different methods described above show some divergence and emphasize the warning given earlier about the ease with which cellulose is degraded. Cellulose from different sources has a different chain-length; in fact, the molecular weight may vary with the conditions prevailing when the polysaccharide was synthesized by the plant.

Further light on the structure of cellulose has been obtained by X-ray studies. The length of the unit cell corresponds to the length of two D-glucopyranose units (Sponsler and Dore 1926, Meyer and Misch 1937). This means that in the cellulose fibre the D-glucose units are arranged in chains parallel to the fibre axis. This is an example of the macro-structure of a material reflecting the micro-structure of the molecules. The distance between hydroxyl groups in adjacent chains is such as to suggest hydrogen bonding between the chains. This may explain the general non-reactivity of native cellulose. X-ray examination of mercerized cellulose shows that the unit cell length is the same, but that adjacent chains have moved further apart, so explaining the greater chemical reactivity of mercerized cellulose, the greater ease with which it may be dyed, and its increased water absorption. Regenerated celluloses (see p. 115) are generally similar to mercerized cellulose.

Cotton fibres are mainly crystalline, but the more reactive, unstretched, regenerated cellulose contains a large proportion of amorphous material. In general, the crystalline micelles are bundles of molecules of indefinite length but with a cross-section of about 50×50 Å. Regions of amorphous material connect these crystalline zones. One molecule may, for example, start in a crystalline region, pass through an amorphous zone, and into another crystalline region.

Chemical methods have been described for determining the

amount of amorphous material in a given sample of cellulose. They all depend on achieving rapid and complete reaction in the amorphous zones before any takes place in the crystalline regions. Since this is difficult it is not surprising that the results vary considerably. Physical methods have also been used. An example is the treatment of a cellulose sample with deuterated water, when all the hydroxyl groups in the amorphous region will be converted into OD. The proportion of OD to OH groups can then be measured by infrared spectrometry (Mann and Marrinan 1956). Such methods show that cotton fibres are largely crystalline (> 70 per cent).

All the properties described above can be explained by considering the conformation of the cellulose molecule, which is composed of β-D-glucopyranose molecules in their preferred CA(D-C1) conformation. This shows how linear molecules are possible.

Regenerated cellulose

The regeneration from cuprammonium solution of cellulose unchanged in chemical properties forms the basis of a process for manufacturing a rayon used in the textile industry. In this way, any form of cellulose whose fibres are too short for direct spinning (e.g. wood cellulose) may be converted into a commercially useful thread.

Another form of regenerated cellulose is prepared from sodium cellulose xanthate. Sodium cellulosate is present in equilibrium when cellulose is added to aqueous sodium hydroxide (e.g. 15 to 20 per cent) at room temperature. Excess solution is pressed out and carbon disulphide is added with cooling to give sodium cellulose xanthate (about two of the three hydroxyl groups in each D-glucose unit are substituted). After 'ripening' (depolymerization to the desired degree) in dilute aqueous sodium hydroxide this solution is forced through fine orifices into a coagulating bath of dilute sulphuric acid to give threads of regenerated cellulose known as viscose rayon. When the solution is forced through a thin slit, the cellulose is regenerated in

$$\text{Cellulose-OH} \underset{}{\overset{\text{NaOH}}{\rightleftharpoons}} \text{Cellulose-ONa} \xrightarrow{\text{CS}_2}$$
$$\text{sodium cellulosate}$$

$$\text{Cellulose-OCS(SNa)} \xrightarrow{\text{H+}} \text{Cellulose-OH} + \text{CS}_2 + \text{Na}^+$$
$$\text{sodium cellulose xanthate}$$

the form of a sheet; this is the process used in the manufacture of 'Cellophane'.

Cellulose derivatives

The derivatives that may be prepared from cellulose are those of the hydroxyl group. Because of its colloidal nature, its general insolubility, and its hydrogen bonding, it reacts less readily than a simple sugar. The very large native cellulose molecules react too slowly to be of value in commercial processes; in addition, the viscosities of solutions of the resulting products are too high to manipulate economically. Therefore, during purification, the cellulose is depolymerized somewhat to give a starting material of the desired molecular weight. During the preparation and purification of the derivative further breakdown of the molecule usually takes place. The main derivatives are esters and ethers, some of which are used for making explosives, textiles, plastics, and lacquers. The degree of substitution of a given derivative has a profound effect on many of its properties, particularly solubility.

Cellulose nitrate is manufactured on a large scale by adding cellulose (linters or wood-pulp) to an excess of a nitrating mixture containing water, nitric acid, and sulphuric acid. The concentrations are adjusted to give the degree of esterification desired: complete substitution is extremely difficult to achieve. If the temperature is kept below 25° the reaction proceeds smoothly and the resultant product is not degraded. In addition to the nitrate groups a small number of rather unstable sulphate groups is present. The product is then boiled with water to improve the stability and to hydrolyse the sulphate groups. The stabilization treatment causes some degradation as is shown by the decrease in the viscosity of solutions of the material. This means that the time of boiling may be regulated to give a wide range of molecular weights. A product containing, on the average, about 2·3 nitrate groups for each D-glucose unit is suitable for plastics and lacquers, but a somewhat higher degree of substitution is required for use in explosives. For making plastics and photographic film base, the cellulose is mixed with camphor which increases the flexibility without undue loss in hardness and tensile strength. Because of this action camphor is said to be a plasticizer for cellulose nitrate: the resultant plastic was originally known as Parkesine (Parkes 1869), but is now commonly called celluloid or Xylonite.

Cellulose triacetate was neglected for many years as a commercially useful material. Recently, however, it has achieved importance as a textile fibre, known in this country as Tricel (Arnel in the U.S.A.). There are three principal processes available for the preparation of triacetate. These are briefly (i) the use of acetic anhydride–acetic acid–sulphuric acid; (ii) the use of acetic anhydride in methylene chloride, with much less sulphuric acid than in the above process; (iii) benzene-acetic anhydride with perchloric acid as catalyst.

Secondary cellulose acetate is prepared by acetylating cellulose with acetic anhydride–sulphuric acid–acetic acid mixtures, followed by slight hydrolysis to remove all the sulphate groups and some of the acetyl groups as well. In this way, a product is obtained which is soluble in cheap solvents, such as acetone. The final degree of substitution is about 2·3 acetyl groups per D-glucose unit. Secondary cellulose acetate is also an important material in the textile and plastics industries.

Other esters such as the *propionate* or *butyrate* may be similarly prepared. Mixed esters, for example cellulose acetate butyrate, are manufactured commercially for use as plastics.

Treatment of cellulose with toluene-*p*-sulphonyl chloride yields *cellulose toluene-*p-*sulphonate*. The tosyl groups on $C_{(6)}$ of cellulose behave as in the sugars in that they, alone, may be replaced quantitatively by iodine with sodium iodide in acetone (see p. 60). This is used as a method for determining the amount of free primary hydroxyl in a partially substituted cellulose derivative.

Ethyl and *methyl* celluloses have been prepared by treating cellulose with aqueous sodium hydroxide and the appropriate dialkyl sulphate or alkyl chloride in an inert atmosphere. The ethyl ether is used for the manufacture of plastics. It is interesting that although cellulose is insoluble in water, the introduction of some ethyl (or methyl) groups, about one per D-glucose unit, gives a material which readily dissolves in water. This is considered to be due to the ethyl groups making the contour of each molecule irregular so that the high degree of hydrogen bonding found in unsubstituted cellulose is no longer possible and so solution in water is facilitated. When the number of alkyl groups is increased, the materials are not soluble in water, but are soluble in alcohols and hydrocarbons as is expected from the increasingly hydrocarbon-like exterior of the ethyl cellulose molecule.

Cross linking of cellulose chains is an important method of introducing crease-resistance into cellulosic fabrics. Reagents that may be used include formaldehyde and 1,3-dichloropropan-2-ol.

CHITIN

Chitin is the chief component of the shells of arthropods such as lobsters, crabs, and shrimps, and of molluscs like oysters and snails. Chitin is most readily obtained from the shells of lobsters by soaking them in cold, dilute hydrochloric acid to remove the calcium carbonate. The thread-like form in which chitin is obtained points to the presence of a linear, long-chain molecule. The molecular weight, as obtained by viscosity measurements, is similar to that of wood-pulp cellulose. Hydrolysis with boiling acid gives D-glucosamine (see p. 75) and acetic acid in

CHITIN

equimolecular amounts. Milder hydrolysis, using an enzyme obtained from the intestines of snails, gives N-acetylglucosamine as the sole product. A disaccharide, chitobiose, has been isolated from the hydrolysis products, and has been shown to be identical with cellobiose except for having an amino group on $C_{(2)}$ of each of the D-glucose units. X-ray studies show that the unit cell has almost the same length as that of cellulose.

STARCH

Starch is the carbohydrate reserve material of plants. It is stored in roots and tubers, as in the potato, and in seeds, as in cereals such as wheat. Starch is more easily hydrolysed than cellulose, and so the importance of the extraction and purification process is even greater. The cereal starches are purified by digesting the grain with dilute aqueous alkali in order to remove the associated protein. The root starches are purer and need only be given a mild bleach with hypochlorite. Even with such gentle treatments it is probable that some slight hydrolysis and oxidation take place; to keep this to a minimum dissolution is carried out under nitrogen. Purifications that involve grinding dry starch in ball-mills, prolonged boiling in the presence of air, or contact with acid must be avoided, or profound degradation results.

The colloidal nature of starch is shown by its forming viscous solutions with very low osmotic pressures. Its constitution has been shown as follows.

1. Acid hydrolysis gives a quantitative yield of D-glucose.

2. Hydrolysis by malt amylases leads to maltose. Yields as high as 80 per cent have been obtained.

3. Treatment with acetyl bromide may be controlled to yield acetobromo-maltose (30 per cent yield). From these results it appears that starch is built up from maltose units in the same way that cellulose is built up from cellobiose.

4. Methylation yields a tri-O-methyl starch which is hydrolysed to 2,3,6-tri-O-methyl-D-glucose together with 5 per cent of 2,3,4,6-tetra-O-methyl-D-glucose.

These results show that starch is made up of D-glucopyranose units linked together from $C_{(1)}$ to $C_{(4)}$, the glucosidic link having the a-configuration. If starch has a linear molecule then the proportion of tetra-O-methyl-D-glucose formed indicates a chain of approximately 20 D-glucose units (Haworth 1932). However, neither starch, nor its derivatives, form threads, and two fractions of starch with widely different properties have been recognized. Also, the molecular weight as determined by physical methods is 10^6 to 10^8, whereas the molecular weight of a molecule of 20 D-glucose units is about 3500.

Many methods have been used to fractionate starch, the most

general method being selective precipitation from starch solutions or dispersions. One is the use of n-butyl alcohol or 'Pentasol' (a mixture of alcohols commercially available in the United States) to precipitate one fraction from an aqueous dispersion. This fraction is obtained in the form of needles, and forms about 28 per cent of corn starch. It is known as *amylose*. A second fraction, called *amylopectin*, can be precipitated from the first mother liquor by the addition of methanol.

A recent small-scale method of isolation and fractionation consists of leaving the starch in contact with dimethyl sulphoxide at room temperature. Addition of n-butanol to the resulting solution precipitates both amylose and amylopectin. These are dissolved by heating briefly in water at 70°. Amylose with average molecular weight of 1.9×10^6 is precipitated from this solution by addition of n-butanol (Killion 1960).

Industrially, fractionation of starch is done by salting out the amylose with magnesium sulphate (Bus, Muetgeert, and Hiemstra 1958). Partial separation results by keeping an aqueous solution of maize starch at a temperature below its boiling point for 8 hours. During this time the amylose (90 per cent pure) separates; evaporation of the residual solution gives amylopectin (87 per cent pure).

An outstanding difference between the two fractions is the tendency of amylose to adsorb other substances. The blue colour that starch gives with iodine is due entirely to the adsorptive power of the amylose present. This property has been used as a quantitative method for the determination of the proportion of amylose in a starch. This method indicates, for instance, that corn starch contains 25 per cent amylose, in good agreement with the value obtained by fractionation. Waxy maize starch, which is almost exclusively amylopectin, has a negligible iodine adsorption.

Amylose. The molecular weight of amylose has been determined by the chemical and physical methods described for cellulose. The physical methods indicate a value corresponding to 1000 to 4000 D-glucose units depending on the source. Methylation and hydrolysis show that amylose is a linear polysaccharide. However, hydrolysis by β-amylase is not always complete, and suggests that units other than the α-$(1\rightarrow4)$ linked D-glucopyranose units may be present.

AMYLOSE

X-ray examination of the amylose–iodine complex has shown that the amylose molecule is in the form of a helix, having about six D-glucose units in each turn and with the iodine atoms lying along the axis of the helix. The conformation of the D-glucose units is thought to be CA (D-D1) (2) or B_3E (D-3B) (3). When starch solutions stand for some time, partial precipitation occurs. This is known as retrogradation, and is due to separation of the amylose fraction. The linear molecules align

(2)   (3)

themselves parallel to each other, and become held together by hydrogen bonds. The aggregates increase in size until they exceed colloidal dimensions and therefore precipitate.

Amylopectin. Physical methods give values ranging as high as over one million D-glucose units for the size of the amylopectin molecule. Methylation and hydrolysis shows that there is one non-reducing end-group for every 20 to 25 D-glucose units; this has been confirmed by the periodate method. These results are only compatible with a highly branched structure. This branched structure explains why amylopectin does not form threads or films, and will not retrograde. Careful analysis of the hydrolysis products shows the presence of about 3 per cent of 2,3-di-O-methyl-D-glucose (Hirst; Freudenberg 1940). This suggests that some of the D-glucose units are joined to others through $C_{(6)}$, as well as $C_{(1)}$ and $C_{(4)}$; these units constitute the branch points. This is confirmed by the isolation of isomaltose and panose a-D-$Gp1$—$6a$-D-$Gp1$—4-D-Gp after partial hydrolysis of amylopectin. The branched structure for amylopectin is

9—I.C.C.

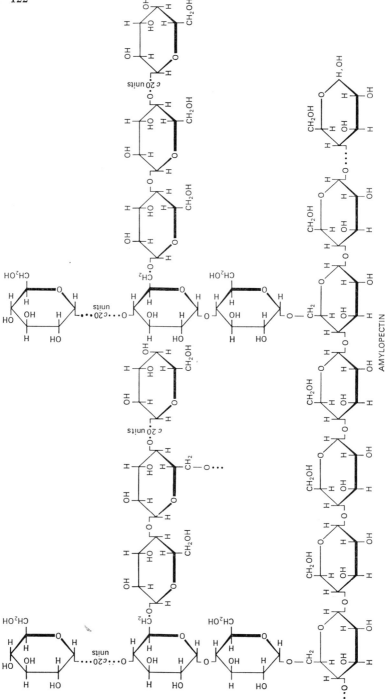

AMYLOPECTIN

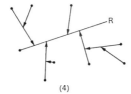

(4)

R = reducing end-group; • = non-reducing end-group

completely random (Meyer 1940), as shown on p. 122 and diagrammatically above (4); this structure has been proved by enzymic degradations (Peat 1954, Hirst 1954).

The processes involved in the enzymic synthesis and degradation and starches is not yet completely understood. It is now considered that amylose is formed from uridine diphosphate glucose by action of the enzyme amylose synthetase (Leloir 1960). A 'primer' is necessary for the process; the smallest molecule that is effective is maltotriose. Branching, to yield amylopectin, is performed by Q-enzyme which breaks a-$(1\rightarrow 4)$ links in amylose and joins one fragment by an a-$(1\rightarrow 6)$ link to another chain. Also involved is D-enzyme which can transfer portions of a-$(1\rightarrow 4)$ linked D-glucose to another similar chain or even to D-glucose itself (Peat 1956). Its purpose may be to supply primer for amylose synthesis.

The a- and β-amylases break the a-$(1\rightarrow 4)$ bond but not the a-$(1\rightarrow 6)$ link. Amylose is thus degraded completely (see however p. 120), whereas amylopectin is broken down to a limit dextrin (see p. 124) in which all the side-chains are stripped as far as the branch points; R-enzyme can break a-$(1\rightarrow 6)$ links (Peat 1951).

The *Schardinger dextrins* are a group of crystalline homologous oligosaccharides, obtained by the action of *Bacillus macerans* amylase on starches (Schardinger 1903). Fractionation of the crude materials yields homogeneous crystalline compounds (Freudenberg 1947, French 1949), the a- and β-dextrins.

Methylation of the a- and β-dextrins followed by hydrolysis gave over 90 per cent of 2,3,6-tri-O-methyl-D-glucose (Freudenberg 1936). Oxidation with periodate required one mole for each D-glucose unit and yielded no formaldehyde or formic acid. These results, coupled with X-ray molecular weight measurements (French 1942), show that the a- and β-dextrins have cyclic molecules of six and seven D-glucose units respectively. Because these cyclic compounds have no end-group they

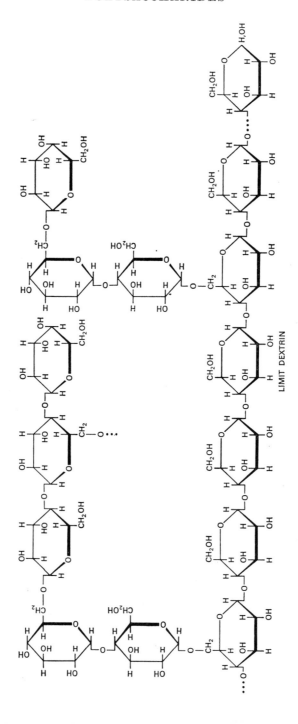

LIMIT DEXTRIN

are more resistant to acid and enzymic hydrolysis than the analogous linear compounds. The α- and β-dextrins are also interesting in that they form complexes with many organic and inorganic materials, including iodine and salts.

GLYCOGEN

Glycogen, the common carbohydrate reserve material of animals, is found in mussels, and in mammalian muscle and liver. It is usually prepared by boiling liver with aqueous alkali to hydrolyse protein, and then precipitating the glycogen with alcohol. As with starch, degradation will occur unless the isolation procedure is very mild.

Acid hydrolysis converts glycogen completely to D-glucose: the optical rotation ($[\alpha]_D = +200°$) suggests the presence of α-linkages. Methylation and periodate oxidation show that glycogen has a branched structure similar to that of amylopectin, but with shorter branches, there being, on average, about twelve glucose units for each non-reducing end-group.

INULIN

Inulin is a reserve polysaccharide that replaces starch in the roots of the Compositae. Good sources are dandelion, dahlia, and Jerusalem artichoke tubers, from which it may be extracted with hot water. The inulin is then isolated by concentrating the aqueous solution and purified by 'recrystallization'. Methylation, followed by hydrolysis, leads to 3,4,6-tri-O-methyl-D-fructofuranose, together with 3·7 per cent of 1,3,4,6-tetra-O-methyl-D-fructofuranose (Haworth 1932). From this it follows that the inulin molecule is unbranched and consists of about

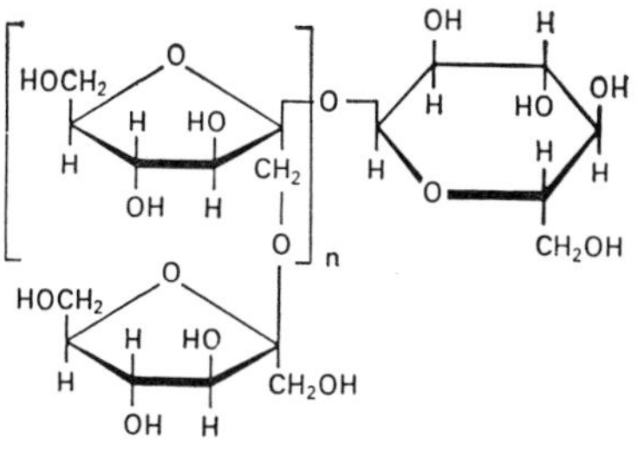

INULIN

thirty D-fructofuranose units linked from $C_{(1)}$ to $C_{(2)}$. The linkage is believed to be β.

More recent work on carefully prepared inulin from dahlias has shown the presence of D-glucose in the inulin molecule. It is believed that one end of the inulin polymer is terminated with a sucrose unit; that is, the end fructose unit is joined through $C_{(2)}$ to a D-glucose unit.

HEMICELLULOSES

The hemicelluloses are a group of substances found associated with cellulose in plant cell-walls. Some of the commonest members of this group are the *xylans*. Esparto grass xylan is composed of chains of β-$(1 \rightarrow 4)$ linked D-xylopyranose units (Haworth, Hirst 1929). This result is partly based on the isolation of xylose, xylobiose, xylotriose, and homologues on acid hydrolysis, and on methylation followed by hydrolysis to only 2,3-di-O-methyl-D-xylose. Other xylans contain different sugar residues, particularly those of L-arabinose, D-glucuronic acid, and its 4-O-methyl ether. However, all xylans are shown to have a common xylose-based backbone because hydrolysis yields xylobiose, etc., and methylation studies yield 2,3-di-O-methyl-D-xylose.

That the L-arabinose units are generally present as furanose non-reducing end-groups, as for example in wheat-flour xylan (Perlin 1951), has been shown by the isolation of 2,3,5-tri-O-methyl-L-arabinose after methylation and hydrolysis. Isolation of some 2-O-methyl-D-xylose suggests that the branches off the xylose backbone are at the 3-position. Two possibilities, however, exist for the nature of the branches; they may be one unit branches with the L-arabinofuranose units joined directly to the backbone (5) or the L-arabinose units may terminate

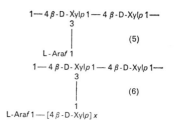

longer xylose-containing branches (6). Enzymic hydrolysis of wheat-straw xylan has led to the isolation of the trisaccharide (7), which is good evidence for a structure of type (5) (Bishop,

(7)

1955). Controlled hydrolysis removes the L-arabinose units without breaking up the main xylose-containing backbone and also supports structure (5).

Some xylans have L-arabinose units in non-terminal positions, for example, those from barley husks and maize (Whistler 1956). Partial hydrolysis gave 2-O-(β-D-xylopyranosyl)-L-arabinose, and methylation studies led to the isolation of 3,5-di-O-methyl-L-arabinofuranose. Structures similar to (5) and (6) are possible for these xylans, with either two unit branches of the above disaccharide or longer xylose-containing branches which are terminated by the disaccharide.

Other xylans including beech-wood xylan contain residues of D-glucuronic acid or its 4-O-methyl ether (Aspinall 1954). These residues always form one-unit branches on the main xylose backbone.

Another common group of hemicelluloses are the *mannans*, one example of which, found in vegetable ivory, is composed of β-(1 → 4) linked D-mannopyranose units. *Glucomannans*, which occur extensively in coniferous woods, are made up of molecules containing both D-glucopyranose and D-mannopyranose residues. Evidence for this has been obtained for some glucomannans which, on acid hydrolysis, gave the disaccharides 4-O-(β-D-glucopyranosyl)-D-mannose and 4-O-(β-D-mannopyranosyl)-D-glucose. It is not yet known whether the D-glucose and D-mannose units occur regularly or randomly along the chain.

DEXTRAN

Dextran is the general name given to the polysaccharides produced by bacteria growing on a substrate of sucrose. The basic skeleton consists of α-(1→ 6) linked D-glucose units; the fine structure is dependent on the particular strain of bacteria used. Much structural work on dextrans has been on the so-called B-512 dextran produced by a substrain of *Leuconostoc mesenteroides*, and the following results are from work on this material.

Methylation and hydrolysis gave 2,4-di-O-methyl-, 2,3,4-tri-O-methyl-, and 2,3,4,6-tetra-O-methyl-D-glucose in the ratio 1:21:1. This suggests a main chain of 1→ 6 linked units with branching of the 1→ 3 type (Rist 1956). Periodate oxidation studies showed that there were 95 per cent of 1→ 6 links, and 5 per cent 1→ 3 links; no evidence for 1→ 4 links was found (Jeanes 1954). These percentages of 1→ 6 and 1→ 3 links were confirmed by degradation of periodate-oxidized dextran by the Smith method (Rist 1954).

Acid hydrolysis of dextran gave isomaltose (Wolfrom 1949). Enzymic hydrolysis gave isomaltose (50 per cent) and isomaltotriose (20 per cent), confirming the structure of the basic skeleton (Jeanes 1953).

The molecular weight of dextrans range from many thousands to the values in the order of 10^7.

The interpretation of these values in terms of detailed fine structure, such as length and spacing of branches, is not yet complete.

These dextrans are used as blood-plasma substitutes and for this purpose need to have a molecular weight of 5–10 × 10^4. These are generally prepared by partial degradation of native dextran.

POLYURONIDES

The polyuronides or poly(uronic acids) are polymers in which the repeating unit is a uronic acid.

One member of this group is alginic acid, obtained as its sodium salt by digestion of certain seaweeds (Laminaria) with aqueous sodium carbonate. Alginic acid is somewhat resistant to acid hydrolysis, but when this is achieved the products are D-mannuronic (mainly) and L-guluronic acids; the relative proportions of the acids vary with the source (F. G. Fischer 1955). Other studies, including methylation and X-ray evidence, show that alginic acid has the uronic acid units linked β-$(1 \to 4)$. Sodium alginate is widely used as a thickening agent in soups, custards, and ice-cream, but has no nutritional value. Pectin may be precipitated from filtered fruit sap by the addition of alcohol. It is a mixture of polysaccharides: the methyl ester of a poly(galacturonic acid), believed to be linked $1 \to 4$, together with an araban and a galactan. Pectin is the substance which causes the setting of jams and jellies. The poly(galacturonic acid) component is believed to be responsible for this property.

GUMS

Plant gums are polysaccharides exuded by certain plants. Well-known examples are gum arabic, gum tragacanth, cherry gum, and mesquite gum.

Acid hydrolysis of any gum yields a complex mixture of uronic acid, generally D-glucuronic acid, together with D-galactose, L-arabinose, and sometimes other sugars including D-xylose. Complete structures have not been elucidated, but the molecules are highly branched.

Gum arabic is produced by unhealthy or damaged trees of the genus *Acacia*. The gum as collected is a salt which, when treated with acid, yields arabic acid. This was hydrolysed by acid to D-galactose, L-arabinose, L-rhamnose, D-glucuronic acid, and 6-O-(β-D-glucopyranosyluronic acid)-D-galactose (Hirst 1951). Dependent on its source the gum contains these sugars in different proportions. Methylation and hydrolysis of arabic acid gave 2,3,4,6-tetra-O-methyl- and 2,4,di-O-methyl-D-galactose, and also 2,3,4-tri-O-methyl-D-glucuronic acid, 2,3,4,-tri-O-methyl-L-rhamnose, 2,3,5-tri-O-methyl-L-arabinose, 2,5-di-O-methyl-L-arabinose, and 2,3-di-O-methyl-D-glucuronic acid. These results led to the proposal of a backbone of D-galactose units linked alternately $1 \to 6$ and $1 \to 3$ (Hirst 1951). However, other methylation studies on a degraded arabic acid in which the aldobiuronic acid side-chains were first removed by the Smith degradation (see p. 109) gave 2,3,4,6-tetra-O-methyl- and 2,4,6-tri-O-methyl-D-galactose, suggesting a backbone containing only $1 \to 3$ links (Smith 1954).

Application of the Barry degradation to arabic acid gave,

after several successive oxidations and phenylhydrazine acetate treatments, a polysaccharide resistant to periodate oxidation. This is further evidence for the $1 \rightarrow 3$ linked backbone (Dillon 1953). The molecular weight of gum arabic as determined by the standard physical methods lies between 2×10^5 and 10^6.

REVIEWS

Methods in structural polysaccharide chemistry, by H. O. Bouveng and B. Lindberg, *Adv. Carbohyd. Chem.* 1960, **15**, 53.

Chitin, by A. B. Foster and J. M. Webber, *Adv. Carbohyd. Chem.* 1960, **15**, 371.

Molecular structure of glycogens, by D. J. Manners, *Adv. Carbohyd. Chem.* 1957, **12**, 261.

The constitution of alginic acid, by D. W. Drummond, E. L. Hirst, and E. Percival, *J. chem. Soc.* 1962, 1208.

The fractionation of starch, by J. Muetgeert, *Adv. Carbohyd. Chem.* 1961, **16**, 299.

Enzymic synthesis and degradation of starch and glycogen, by D. J. Manners, *Adv. Carbohyd. Chem.* 1962, **17**, 371.

Physical properties of solutions of polysaccharides, by W. Banks and C. T. Greenwood, *Adv. Carbohyd. Chem.* 1963, **18**, 357.

Structure and some reactions of cellulose, by D. M. Jones, *Adv. Carbohyd. Chem.* 1964, **19**, 219.

Wood hemicelluloses, by T. E. Timmell, *Adv. Carbohyd. Chem.* 1964, **19**, 247 and 1965, **20**, 410.

Chemical synthesis of polysaccharides, by I. J. Goldstein and T. L. Hullar, *Adv. Carbohyd. Chem.* 1966, **21**, 431.

Polysaccharides of marine algae, by S. Peat and J. R. Turvey, *Fortschr. Chem. org. Natstoffe*, 1965, **23**, 1.

15

PHYSICAL METHODS

PHYSICAL methods can be used for separating different substances, and also for help in identifying and characterizing unknown substances. Detailed descriptions of the underlying physical principles will be found in the references listed at the end of the chapter. Emphasis will be placed on the application of the various methods to carbohydrate chemistry.

Paper chromatography is used extensively in carbohydrate chemistry. A very small amount of a mixture is placed at one end of a strip of filter paper, which is then eluted with a homogeneous mixture of water and organic solvent(s), such as butanol:ethanol:water or pyridine:ethyl acetate:water. The eluent is allowed to flow up, down, or across the paper, causing the original spot to separate into a row of spots, each spot generally corresponding to one component of the mixture. Separations usually take several hours. These spots, often colourless, are then located by spraying the strip with some reagent; for example, ammoniacal silver nitrate gives dark-coloured spots with reducing sugars, and aqueous sodium periodate followed by Schiff's reagent gives pink spots for compounds containing a-glycol groups.

This technique has two main applications; first, the separation of complex mixtures, such as those obtained from the hydrolyses of polysaccharides, and second, the identification and characterization of sugars and their derivatives. The distance moved by a compound divided by the distance moved by the solvent front is characteristic and is called the R_f value of the compound. This value may be affected by external factors such as temperature, and compounds are better characterized by comparing their distance moved with that of a standard substance that is run alongside the mixture under examination. Thus, R_{Rh} values refer to distances moved relative to those moved by L-rhamnose. Chromatography on thick paper can be used for separations on the milligram scale.

Thin layer chromatography (tlc) enables the techniques of

paper chromatography to be applied to adsorbents other than paper. A thin layer of adsorbent, such as silica or alumina, is spread on a glass plate and after activation of the layer, a small amount of the mixture under investigation is placed at one end. The mixture is eluted by a suitable solvent (or mixture of solvents) in a closed vessel by the ascending method. The separated substances are generally located either by placing in iodine vapour, which gives yellow-brown spots, or by spraying with concentrated sulphuric acid in ethanol, which gives grey-black spots. Selective sprays such as those described under paper chromatography may also be used.

A common size of glass plate for tlc is 5 × 20 cm but microscope slides can be used.

The great advantage of tlc is that separations take only 20–40 min (the solvent is usually allowed to travel 10 cm from the origin). It is a good method for monitoring reactions and for testing the homogeneity of purified substances, as well as trial runs before column chromatography. Thick layers of adsorbent on large plates (40 × 20 cm or 100 × 20 cm) can be used for separations or purifications on a preparative scale.

The use of thin layers of cellulose on glass has recently been introduced as an alternative to paper chromatography.

Column chromatography is used widely for separating the constituents of mixtures of sugars and derivatives on a larger scale than is feasible by paper chromatography. A solution of the mixture is placed on a column of adsorbent, which is then eluted by organic solvents, the least strongly adsorbed compound leaving the column first. Fractions may be collected and the compounds isolated by evaporation of the solutions. Common adsorbents are cellulose powder, alumina, charcoal, and silicic acid.

Gas-liquid (vapour-phase) chromatography (glc or vpc) enables minute quantities of volatile substances to be separated. Their vapour, dispersed in an inert carrier gas, is passed through a heated column of a non-volatile stationary phase, such as silicone oil, on an inert solid support like glass beads. The least strongly-retained compounds emerge first from the end of the column. Sugars and their glycosides are too involatile for examination by this technique, but their trimethylsilyl ethers (see p. 45) are very suitable and have found wide use; methods are now available for conversion of very small quantities of sugars into such derivatives. Other derivatives that have been used include acetates, trifluoroacetates, and methyl ethers; the last-mentioned are often obtained during structural investigation of polysaccharides (see p. 108). The components of a mixture can be analysed quantitatively by this technique.

Electrophoresis (*ionophoresis*) utilizes the different mobilities on paper of ionic complexes of sugars, such as those with the borate or molybdate ions, when subjected to a high voltage. As in paper chromatography, the distance moved is characteristic. The formation of the ionic complexes is dependent on the con-figuration and conformation of the sugar and on the particular ions used. Compounds that run close together as complexes with one ion may be well separated as the complexes of some other ion.

Ultraviolet spectroscopy has found little use in carbohydrate chemistry since neither the sugars nor their more usual deriva-tives contain chromophoric groups (see, however, p. 56).

Infrared spectrometry measures the absorption by the molecule of infrared radiation of different frequencies. The resulting spectrum having many bands of various intensities acts as a 'finger-print' for the molecule. An unknown compound may be identified by comparing its spectrum with that of an authentic compound. If complete identification is not possible the pre-sence or absence of various functional groups can usually be established. For example, the presence or absence of OH or NH groups can be investigated by inspecting the spectrum in the 3600–3200 cm^{-1} region. The absorption of the C=O group in O-acetyl and N-acetyl groups occurs at different frequencies and so each of these groups can be identified in the presence of the other. The ring size of sugar derivatives can be determined by the presence or absence of certain bands (S. A. Barker 1954). The spectra of carbohydrates have a characteristic group of bands at 1250–1050 cm^{-1} due to the large number of C—O bonds in their molecules. This feature can be useful in a pre-liminary investigation of reaction products. Infrared spectro-scopy is also useful for monitoring reactions. For example, methylation of a carbohydrate can be followed by the decrease in the hydroxyl band to zero absorption when methylation is complete; reduction of a keto-group can be similarly monitored by following the disappearance of the carbonyl absorption band.

Important negative information may also be obtained from an infrared spectrum. If the characteristic absorptions of a functional group are absent from the spectrum of a molecule, then that functional group is not present in the molecule. The shift of the hydroxyl stretching frequency caused by hydrogen-bonding has been of great value in studying this phenomenon.

Proton magnetic resonance spectroscopy has been used successfully in carbohydrate chemistry, particularly in assigning conformations to cyclic molecules. The positions of the signals from protons in various environments are usually measured relative to the signal given by tetramethylsilane, $(CH_3)_4Si$, (TMS), the so-called τ-scale on which the TMS signal is 10·00. One very useful feature of a proton magnetic resonance spectrum is that the ratio of areas under the absorption bands is the ratio of protons in each group. The magnetic field experienced by different protons is slightly different due to the local shielding or deshielding by neighbouring atoms or groups. Thus in the spectra of sugar glycosides the signal from the anomeric acetal proton is generally separated from those from the other protons, occurring about 0·5–1·0 ppm lower. Acetylation of a hydroxyl group causes the signal from the proton on the same carbon atom to be shifted to values of about 1·0 ppm lower. As well as deductions that can be made from the position of the signals, useful stereochemical information results from the splitting of the bands, since protons on adjacent carbons mutually split each other's signals. On a six-membered ring, such as a pyranose ring, the magnitude of the splitting is characteristic of the protons relative stereochemistry, e.g. axial–axial or axial–equatorial. Such splittings were used to investigate the preferred conformations of hexopyranose and pentopyranose polyacetates (Lemieux 1958). This work has been extended in recent years to investigate the preferred conformation of a wide variety of carbohydrate derivatives (see, for example, the work of Coxon, Foster, Hall, Lemieux, and Perlin, 1964–8).

Mass spectrometry is a powerful physical tool being used in organic chemistry. The fragmentation pattern resulting from the electron bombardment of a molecule is recorded by the mass spectrometer as positive ions on a mass/charge (m/e) ratio. The molecular ion $(M^+;$ removal of one electron) can sometimes be recognized; from it the exact molecular weight can be calculated, and hence the molecular formula determined. The spectrum of fragment ions constitutes a 'finger-print' for the molecule and has the advantage that it is obtained from the use of less than 1 mg of material. The strongest peak is called the base peak and the other peaks are expressed as a percentage of it. Careful study of a series of similar compounds enables the postulation of a fragmentation pattern and the identification of characteristic peaks for certain types of compound or groups within a molecule. The main relevant classes of compounds studied so far have been methylated glycosides (Kochetkov 1963 on), polyacetates and isopropylidene acetals (Bieman 1963–4), amino-sugars and deoxy-sugars (DeJongh and Hanessian 1965), and anhydro-sugars (Heyns 1966). For the carbohydrate chemist, this technique has the disadvantage that it is not very sensitive to stereochemical differences.

X-ray spectroscopy, as in other fields, has been used to determine the structures, conformations, and absolute configurations of molecules in the solid state (e.g. ascorbic acid (p. 95) and sucrose (p. 101)).

Optical measurements are possible because the sugars and their derivatives are optically active. The optical rotation of solutions of sugars or their derivatives at the wavelength of the sodium D-line provides a physical constant ($[a]_D$) for identifying and characterizing the compound, and for assessing its purity. Empirical rules relating structure and rotational values have been devised (Whiffen 1956, Bose and Chatterjee 1958) (see also p. 25). Optical rotatory dispersion has not yet been widely applied because of lack of sugar derivatives containing suitable absorbing functional groups but those for which results have been reported include keto-sugars and thionocarbonates. Studies of the far ultraviolet rotatory dispersion of free sugars has led to the proposal of rules predicting the contribution of substituents at different positions on the ring (Listowsky 1966).

REVIEWS AND FURTHER READING

Paper chromatography of carbohydrates and related compounds, by G. N. Kowkabany, *Adv. Carbohyd. Chem.* 1954, **9**, 303.

Column chromatography of sugars and their derivatives, by W. W. Binkley, *Adv. Carbohyd. Chem.* 1955, **10**, 55.

Zone electrophoresis of carbohydrates, by A. B. Foster, *Adv. Carbohyd. Chem.* 1957, **12**, 81.

Optical rotatory dispersion, by C. Djerassi (McGraw-Hill, 1960).

Paper electrophoresis of carbohydrates, by H. Weigel, *Adv. Carbohyd. Chem.* 1963, **18**, 61.

Crystal structure analysis in carbohydrate chemistry, by G. A. Jeffrey and R. D. Rosenstein, *Adv. Carbohyd. Chem.* 1964, **19**, 7.

Infrared spectroscopy and carbohydrate chemistry, by H. Spedding, *Adv. Carbohyd. Chem.* 1964, **19**, 23.

Nuclear magnetic resonance, by L. D. Hall, *Adv. Carbohyd. Chem.* 1964, **19**, 51.

Gas–liquid chromatography of carbohydrate derivatives, by C. T. Bishop, *Adv. Carbohyd. Chem.* 1964, **19**, 95.

Some applications of nuclear magnetic resonance spectroscopy in natural product chemistry, by L. M. Jackman, *Fortschr. Chem. org. Natstoffe* 1965, **23**, 315.

AUTHOR INDEX

SUBJECT INDEX

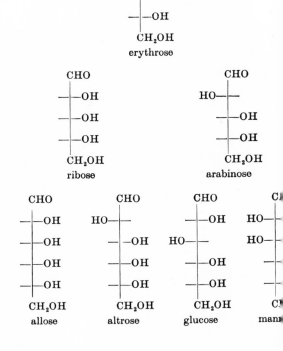

```
        CHO
      —|—OH
      —|—OH
       CH₂OH
      erythrose
```

```
        CHO                          CHO
      —|—OH                    HO—|—
      —|—OH                        —|—OH
      —|—OH                        —|—OH
       CH₂OH                        CH₂OH
       ribose                      arabinose
```

```
    CHO         CHO          CHO          C
  —|—OH     HO—|—         —|—OH      HO—|—
  —|—OH       —|—OH    HO—|—         HO—|—
  —|—OH       —|—OH       —|—OH         —|—
  —|—OH       —|—OH       —|—OH         —|—
   CH₂OH       CH₂OH       CH₂OH          C
   allose      altrose     glucose       man
```